ECONOMIC APPLICATIONS OF THE
THEORY OF GRAPHS

Tracts on Mathematics and Its Applications

Edited by Jacob T. Schwartz, Institute of Mathematical Sciences, New York University

Volume 1

Giuseppe Avondo-Bodino, ECONOMIC APPLICATIONS OF THE THEORY OF GRAPHS

Additional volumes in preparation

ECONOMIC APPLICATIONS OF THE THEORY OF GRAPHS

by Giuseppe Avondo-Bodino

Center for Operations Research
Luigi Bocconi University, Milan
and Faculty of Economics and Commerce
University of Urbino, Urbino, Italy

G
B

GORDON AND BREACH
SCIENCE PUBLISHERS, NEW YORK

Preface

The purpose of this book is to acquaint the reader with a group of economic problems relating to business management and to economic policy in general. The author intends to solve them by means of a method based strictly on topological considerations. This method frequently affords considerable advantages over the analytic procedures which, generally, are better known and, hence, applied more extensively.

The list below is presented to the reader for orientation purposes. For this reason it does not claim to be complete. On the other hand, the reader will be able to detect in each problem much of practical interest.

These are the problems to be considered in this book:

The Transport Problem. It is assumed that specific amounts of certain goods situated in various localities must be transported to other assigned localities. The problem is to devise the optimum transport procedure, that is, the procedure which reduces operational costs to a minimum.

The foregoing statement may be too general; it can, however, be supplemented by the following, more specific, statements, which, however, differ from each other in certain characteristics.

(*a*) Monge's Problem. In a given area there are distributed several masses which must be transported to

v

another assigned area, with the condition that the overall transportation costs are to be reduced to a minimum.

This statement, related to the embarkment problem, will not be pursued in the following.[1]

(b) Hitchcock's Problem.[2] Given m ports of embarkation and n ports of destination, we are to determine the routes of the ships carrying separable merchandise; the cost of individual crossings, the number of ships originally present at the various ports of embarkation, and the quantity of goods required at the various ports of destination being known. The solution consists in minimizing cost.

(c) Orden's Problem.[3] Certain merchandise is distributed in a prearranged manner. This distribution is such that in some locales under consideration the demand exceeds the supply, while in other areas, supply is in excess of demand. If we assume some unit cost of transportation from one locale to another and that the quantity of merchandise in excess equals the total demand, we may then determine the minimum cost of satisfying the demand.

Optimum Personnel Assignment Problem. Following is the statement in accordance with the model of Votaw and

---

[1] See Monge, *Dèblai et Ramblai*, *Mémoires de l'Académie des Sciences*, 1781.

[2] F. L. Hitchcocks, "The Distribution of a Product from Several Sources to Numerous Localities," *Journal of Mathematical Physics* **20** (1941).

[3] A. Orden, "The Transshipment Problem," *Management Science* **2** (1956).

Orden:[1] There are n workers to be assigned to n different machines, and it is assumed that the output of each worker with regard to each machine is known. We are to determine the optimum assignment to achieve maximum total output.

The Warehouse Problem.[2] We assume the capacity of a warehouse, the quantity of merchandise originally placed in storage, the unit purchase and sales price at some time, and the unit cost of storage to be known. We want to determine the quantities of merchandise which have to be purchased and sold at various times $t_k \ldots t_n$ in order to realize maximum profit during a specific period of time, subject to the condition that, at the end of the period under consideration, the warehouse stock will be equal to the amount originally placed in storage.

Problems Connected with the Economic Model of Industrial Interdependences. In a given market there are n industries producing a total of m goods. It is known that, on the basis of appropriate hypotheses, Leontief's method of matrix analysis enables us to predict the quantities which should be produced by the various industries to deliver the products required in the planned amounts.

The theory of graphs enables us to solve the following problem: The initial stocks of the various products being

---

[1] D. F. Votaw and A. Orden, "The Personnel Assignment Problem," *Scoop Symposium on Linear Inequalities and Programming*, Washington, 1952.

[2] A. S. Cahn, "The Warehouse Problem," *Bulletin of the American Mathematical Society* **54** (1948).

known, we are to determine the rate at which individual industries must produce so that at the end of the period under consideration the stocks will reach preassigned values.

In order that the treatment of this presentation be as self-contained as possible, we shall first of all expound some notions concerning sets, vectors, and matrices. Thereafter, we will deal with that part of the theory of graphs which we consider most suited to our purposes. We shall conclude by describing in detail the solution of the problems described above, emphasizing, whenever the occasion arises, the advantages afforded by our method over those presented by analytical solutions.

Contents

III. Transport Networks

IV. Economic Applications

CONTENTS

CHAPTER I

Sets, Vectors, and Matrices

Section 1. Sets

The notion of *set* is regarded as a fundamental concept and hence requires no definition.   We can, however, say that any group of members, finite or infinite in number, represents a set.

Any of the members constituting a set is called an *element* of the set.   In order to indicate that an element a belongs to a set A we write:

$$a \in A$$

The *empty set* is the set containing no elements.

If sets A and B are such that each element of A is also an element of B and vice versa, we say that A and B *c oincide* and write:

$$A = B.$$

If, on the other hand, the elements of A belong to B, but some elements of B do not belong to A, then we write:

$$A \subset B$$

and say that A is a *proper sub-set* of B.

The expression $A \subseteq B$ comprises both of the above cases.

We write:

$$A = \{a \epsilon B / a \text{ has the property P}\}$$

in order to show that A is a sub-set of B whose members have a certain property P.

Section 2. Operations with Sets

1. The *intersection* of two sets is a set formed by the elements common to two given sets. In this case we write:

$$A \cap B \text{ or } B \cap A$$

If $A \cap B$ is empty, the two sets are called *disjoint*.

2. A *logical sum* of two sets is a set whose elements belong to A or B or both. Then we write:

$$A \cup B$$

3. The *Cartesian product* of two sets A and B is the set consisting of all the pairs (a,b) such that $a \in A$ and $b \in B$. In this case we write:

$$A \times B$$

If $A \subset D$ the elements of D which do not belong to A form a *complementary set of A with respect to D* denoted by the symbol

$$C_D (A).$$

We have the following properties:

$$A \cap (B \cup C) = (A \cap B) \cup (A \cap C)$$
$$A \cup (B \cap C) = (A \cup B) \cap (A \cup C)$$
$$C_D(A \cup B) = C_D(A) \cap C_D(B)$$
$$C_D(A \cap B) = C_D(A) \cup C_D(B)$$

Section 3. Rèlations and Correspondences

Given two sets A and B (which may coincide), we consider their Cartesian product $A \times B$. In this new set let us consider a sub-set consisting of the members of A, which have a certain property, and of members of B, which have some other property. Thus we say that a certain relation has been established between A and B and we write:

$$b \, R \, a$$

where R is a symbol denoting the sub-set $A \times B$ described above. If we write $a \, R^{-1} \, b$ we say that R^{-1} is the *inverse* of relation R.

If A' is the set of the elements of A belonging to at least one pair of the set R, and B' is an analogous set relative to B, we say that A' is the *domain* of R, and B' is its *co-domain*.

If a, a', and a'' are members of A and if there exists between them a relation R such that:

1) $a \, R \, a$ (reflexive property)

2) if $a \, R \, a'$
   also $a' \, R \, a$ (symmetric property)

3) if $a \, R \, a'$
   and $a' \, R \, a''$ (transitive property)
   also $a \, R \, a''$

then R is called an *equivalence relation*.

An equivalence relation between elements of a set A makes it possible to partition the set A into sub-sets called equivalence classes relative to R. These classes are disjoint by pairs and each element of A belongs to one and only one of them.

If two sets A and B (possibly coinciding) are given, and we consider the sub-set C of the set $A \times B$ in such a way that each member of A belongs only to *one pair* of C, then we state that a *correspondence (transformation)* has been established between sets A and B, and we write: $b = f(a)$.

A correspondence (whereby only one b corresponds to an element a) may be such that it relates only one a to a given element b. In this case we state that there is a *one-to-one correspondence* and write

$$A \longleftrightarrow B$$

Then the correspondence between B and A, written $a = f(b)$, is called an *inverse correspondence* of the former.

DEFINITION: A set A is said to be *infinite* if it is possible to establish a one-to-one correspondence between A and a proper subset B of A.

Section 4. Sets of Points

An ordered n-tuple set of real numbers can be regarded as the set of coordinates of a point in n-dimensional space.

If two points A $(a_1, a_2, \ldots, a_n)$ and B$(b_1, b_2, \ldots, b_n)$ are given, the real number

$$d(\text{AB}) = \sqrt{\textstyle\sum_{i=1}^{n}(a_i - b_i)^2}$$

is called the *distance* between the points.

Such a definition of *distance* satisfies the following conditions:

    1) $d(\text{AB}) = d(\text{BA})$
    2) $d(\text{AB}) > 0$ if A $\neq$ B
       $d(\text{AB}) = 0$ if A $=$ B
    3) $d(\text{AC}) \leqslant d(\text{AB}) + d(\text{BC})$

This definition of distance characterizes Euclidean hyperspaces. The set S of points P with the coordinates

$$x_i = \lambda\, a_i + \mu\, b_i \qquad\qquad i = 1, 2, \ldots n$$
$$\lambda + \mu = 1 \qquad\qquad \lambda \geq 0 \quad \mu \geq 0$$

is called the *segment* between endpoints A, B. A set of points P where

$$d\,(P\,\bar{P}) < s$$

is called a *hypersphere* with a radius s and a center $\bar{P}$ (it is also called the circumference of $\bar{P}$ with radius s). A set of points P where

$$|x_i - \bar{x}_i| < s \qquad\qquad i = 1, 2, \ldots n$$

is called a *hypersquare* with center $\bar{P}$ and semiside s.

A set of points is *bounded* if, having fixed any point O, there exists a real number N such that the distance from O to all the points of the set is less than N.

A *point of accumulation* of a set A is a point P such that every neighborhood of P contains points of A distinct from P.   If P∈A and P is not a point of accumulation, P is an *isolated point*.

A set of points is *closed* if all of its accumulation points belong to the set; a set A is *open* if the set of all points not in A is closed.

The set of all the points of accumulation of a set A is called a derived set of A.

A set coinciding with its derived set is *perfect*.

A point P of the set A is called

1) An *interior* point if there exists a neighborhood around P contained in A;

2) An *exterior* point if there exists a neighborhood around P into which points of A do not fall;

3) A *boundary* point in all the other cases.

A *space* is a perfect set where each point is a point of accumulation of interior points.

A space is *connected* if two interior points selected arbitrarily can be connected by means of a polygonal line constituted by interior points of the space.

A set is *convex* if the segment connecting two of its points belong entirely to the set.

If A and B are convex sets, then also A ∩ B is convex.

A space is said to be *strictly convex at* A if A is a boundary point and any segment joining A to another boundary point B contains no other boundary points.

A space has a *convex structure* if it is strictly convex at any point of its boundary.

In a given non-convex space D the sum of points belonging to segments with endpoints contained in D is called the *convex covering* of D.

Section 5. Vectors

Vectors are directed segments; their *components* are real numbers associated with the projections of a vector on the coordinate axes. If a vector is directed from the origin, its components coincide with the coordinates of its end point.

Hence, an ordered n-tuple set of real numbers can be interpreted as the set of components of a vector applied at the origin of the coordinate axes.

If a_i and b_i are the corresponding components of two vectors **A**, **B**, we have:

1) $\mathbf{A} = \mathbf{B}$ if $a_i = b_i$ $i = 1, 2, \ldots n$

2) $\lambda \mathbf{A} = (\lambda a_1, \lambda a_2, \ldots \lambda a_n)$ λ a real number

3) $\mathbf{C} = \mathbf{A} + \mathbf{B}$ $\mathbf{C} = (a_1 + b_1, a_2 + b_2, \ldots)$

The *modulus* of a vector is the real positive number

$$\text{mod } \mathbf{A} = \sqrt{\sum_{i=1}^{n} a_i^2}$$

Given m vectors $\mathbf{A}_1, \mathbf{A}_2, \ldots, \mathbf{A}_m$, we say that the vector $\mathbf{A} = \sum_{s=1}^{m} \lambda_s \mathbf{A}_s$ is a *linear combination* of the given vectors, and the real numbers λ_s are the *coefficients* of the combination.

If the numbers λ_s (not all equalling zero) can be so chosen that $\sum \lambda_s \mathbf{A}_s = 0$, vectors $\mathbf{A}_s$ are *linearly dependent;* otherwise they are *linearly independent*.

The set of all vectors of an n-dimensional space constitutes a vector space R_n. n linearly independent vectors D_i, constitute a basis for space R_n in the sense that any other vector of R_n can be obtained as their linear combination:

$$A = \sum_{i=1}^{n} \lambda_i D_i$$

A convenient basis for R_n is given by the n vectors

$$L_1 = (1, 0, 0, \ldots, 0)$$

$$L_2 = (0, 1, 0, \ldots, 0)$$

$$\cdot \quad \cdot \quad \cdot$$

$$L_n = (0, 0, 0, \ldots, 1)$$

which are linearly independent.

Section 6. Matrices

A (m, n)-type matrix consists of $m \times n$ numbers arranged in a rectangular array. The most convenient arrangement consists in writing these numbers (matrix elements) in m rows and n columns. The generic element is designated by a_{ik} where the first index determines the row and the second determines the column; the matrix is indicated by

$$A (m, n) = \|a_{ik}\|$$

From a given matrix $A (m,n)$, a matrix of (n,m)-type, called the *transpose* of $A (m,n)$ may be obtained by interchanging rows and columns. It will be denoted by $A'(n,m) = \|a_{ki}\|$.

If two matrices $A(m,r)$ and $B(m,s)$ are given, we can obtain a matrix $C(m,r+s)$ by properly combining the first two. A and B are submatrices of C.

Likewise, from D (r,n) and E (s,n) we can obtain F $(r + s,n)$ by proper combination.

We can write, respectively:

$$\|A \mid B\| \; ; \; \left\|\frac{D}{E}\right\|$$

Since a vector (line vector) can be regarded as a matrix of the type $(1,n)$, we may also consider a matrix A (m,n) obtained by combining m line vectors (horizontal vectors). In the same way a matrix $A(m,n)$ may be obtained by combining n column vectors (m,s).

Section 7. Operations with Matrices

Following are the relationships between matrices of the same type[1]:

1. $A = B$ if $a_{ik} = b_{ik}$
2. $A > B$ if $a_{ik} > b_{ik}$
3. $A \geqslant B$ if $a_{ik} > b_{ik}$ at least for one pair, and if all pairs for which this relationship does not hold are equal.

Sum and Difference

If two matrices of the same type are given, we have:

$$C = A \pm B \quad \text{if} \quad c_{ik} = a_{ik} \pm b_{ik}$$

---

[1] Two matrices are of the same or similar type if they have the same number of rows and columns, respectively.

The sum and difference of similar matrices enjoy the same properties as the sum and difference of numbers.

Scalar product

Given a real number λ the scalar product of A for λ is the matrix B with elements $b_{ik} = \lambda\, a_{ik}$.

Products of matrices

With two given matrices $A(m,r)$ and $B(r,n)$, the product $C = A \cdot B$ is the matrix with the elements

$$c_{ik} = \sum_{j=1}^{n} a_{ij}\, b_{jk}$$

It should be noted that the number of columns of the first matrix and the number of rows of the second must be equal.

Moreover, the commutative property AB = BA *is generally not valid.*

Valid are, however:

the distributive property
$$A(B + C) = AB + AC;$$

the associative property
$$A \times (B \times C) = (A \times B) \times C.$$

In particular, it is found that the product of two vectors **X,Y** (which correspond, respectively, to a line and a column vector) is the number

$$X\, Y = \sum_{1}^{n} x_i\, y_i;$$

and

$$X \widetilde{X} = \sum_1^n x_i{}^2 = (\text{mod } X)^2$$

If

$$M = \left\| \frac{A \mid B}{C \mid D} \right\| \quad \text{and} \quad M' = \left\| \frac{A' \mid B'}{C' \mid D'} \right\|$$

we have

$$M + M' = \left\| \frac{A + A' \mid B + B'}{C + C' \mid D + D'} \right\| \; ;$$

$$M \cdot M' = \left\| \frac{AA' + BC' \mid AB' + BD'}{CA' + DC' \mid CB' + DE'} \right\|$$

provided that the above operations are permissible in accordance with what has been stated above.

Given a non-degenerate square matrix A (that is, a matrix whose determinant is different from zero), it is possible to determine a matrix called the *inverse matrix of* A which is designated by the symbol A^{-1}; it is defined by the relationship

$$A^{-1} \cdot A = A \times A^{-1} = I$$

Matrix I is called the *unit matrix* and its elements are defined by the relationships

$$a_{ij} = 0 \text{ for } i \neq j$$
$$a_{ij} = 1 \text{ for } i = j$$

The *cofactor* of a_{ij} is the determinant of the submatrix X obtained by deleting the ith row and jth column of A, multiplied by $(-1)^{i+j}$. The elements of the inverse matrix are given by

$$a_{ij} = \frac{A_{ji}}{|A|}$$

where A_{ji} is the cofactor of a_{ji} in A, and $|A|$ is the determinant.

CHAPTER II

General Data on Graphs

Section 1. Definition of Graphs

Let us consider a set X consisting of elements called points, and a law which permits us to introduce a correspondence T between each element of X and any of its sub-sets. We designate the latter by the symbol Tx, where x is the generic element of X. The pair "set X" and "correspondence T" defines a graph.

The set X may be finite or infinite, but in both cases the graph may be finite. This case occurs when, due to correspondence T, each element x of X corresponds to a finite sub-set of X.

Since the most appropriate representation of a graph is obviously the geometrical one, the elements of X will be represented by points, and the correspondence T can be

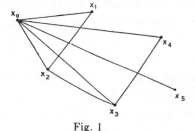

Fig. 1

symbolized by means of segments (eventually directed ones) connecting x with the elements of the sub-set Tx.

For example Fig. 1 shows a graph defined by the set

$$X = \{x_0, x_1, x_2, x_3, x_4, x_5\}$$

and by the correspondence T characterized by

$$Tx_0 = \{x_1, x_2, x_3, x_4, x_5\}$$
$$Tx_1 = \{x_0, x_2\}$$
$$Tx_2 = \{x_0, x_1, x_3\}$$
$$Tx_3 = \{x_0, x_2, x_4\}$$
$$Tx_4 = \{x_0, x_3\}$$
$$Tx_5 = \{x_0\}$$

The graph is regarded as *symmetrical* if, by considering two points x_i and x_j, it is found that if x_i belongs to Tx_j, x_j must necessarily belong to Tx_i.

Where this is not the case for all the pairs of points involved, the graph is regarded as *asymmetrical*. A pair of points x_i and x_j (where x_i belongs to Tx_j or vice versa) constitutes a *line* of the graph; if in addition, an order is attributed to the pair of points, then the latter is called an *arc* of the graph and the graph will be termed a *directed graph*.

Lines are represented by means of segments having as endpoints x_i and x_j; to represent the corresponding arc, it is necessary to show its orientation by means of an arrow.

Two separate points x_i and x_j are adjacent if they determine an arc (or a line).

Two separate arcs are *adjacent* if they have an endpoint in common.

A sequence of arcs where the terminal point of one arc is the initial point of the subsequent one, is called a *course*. A course is determined either by the sequence of arcs constituting it or by means of the sequence of the end-points of the arcs.

If the initial and the terminal points of a course coincide, a *circuit* is formed.

The *length* of a course or a circuit is given by the number of arcs which constitute them. A circuit of unit length is called a *loop* (it links a point with itself).

If we consider lines rather than arcs, the analogue of a course is a *chain*, and the analogue of a circuit is a *cycle*.

A cycle can be:
simple, if the lines involved are different from one another;
compound, if the contrary is the case;
elementary, if each point of the cycle is intercepted only once.

The reader will have noticed that the definitions for line, chain, and cycle differ from the corresponding definitions of arc, course, and circuit only insofar as in the latter a direction is essentially taken into consideration.

A graph is *connected* if there exists a chain which makes it possible to pass from one to the other of two points on a graph regardless of how they have been selected.

A *disconnected* graph is one constituted of several connected graphs.

A *strongly connected* graph is one where each pair of points can be regarded as the extreme points of a course.

At this point it is possible to modify slightly the definition of symmetrical graphs given above by saying that, in the case of symmetry, each pair of adjacent points defines two arcs of opposite orientations.

On the other hand, we state, that a graph is asymmetrical if there are pairs of adjacent points linked by arcs having only one orientation.

A graph is *complete* if each pair of points is connected by at least one arc.

A graph having at least two points, which is finite, connected, and without cycles, is called a *tree*.

A graph is said to be one *with multiple lines* if at least one pair of points are connected by different lines.

A finite, connected graph without loops is called a *network* if the following conditions are true:

a) it is directed and there exist two points x_0 and x_n such that

$$T^{-1}x_0 = 0$$
$$Tx_n \ = 0.$$

According to our definition x_0 is the *initial point* of the the graph, while x_n is its *terminal point*.

b) each arc of the graph has been associated with a positive number equal to or greater than zero, which is termed its *capacity*.

The following definition of *independent cycles* will be useful: in a graph with multiple lines, assign an arbitrary orientation to individual lines, then take a cycle and consider the difference between the number of times a line is described in the assigned orientation and the number of times it is described in the opposite orientation.

If c_i is this difference calculated for the ith line, let us associate with the cycle the vector whose components are the differences c_i. We say that the two cycles are *independent* if the two associated vectors are linearly independent.

In order better to explain the above definitions it will be helpful to refer to the following figures.

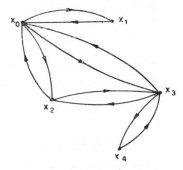

Fig. 2a

Figure 2a shows a symmetrical graph; the sequence of adjacent arcs x_0x_2, x_2x_3, x_3x_4 constitutes a course which is designated by the symbol (x_0, x_2, x_3, x_4).

Figure 2b shows an asymmetrical graph (not all of the adjacent points are connected by arcs oriented in two inverse directions). The sequence of arcs x_0x_1, x_1x_2, $x_2x_3, x_3x_4, x_4x_5, x_5x_0$ constitutes a circuit with length $l = 6$.

Circuit $Tx_1 = x_1$ constitutes a loop.

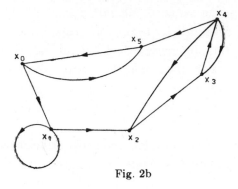

Fig. 2b

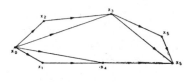

Fig. 2c

Figure 2c represents a network; the initial point is at x_0 while the terminal is at x_6; we assume here that each of the arcs is associated with its proper capacity.

Fig. 2d

Figure 2d shows a graph with multiple lines. Chemical structure formulas are interesting examples of such graphs, and the theory of graphs proved to be extremely useful for the calculation of the number of isomers of a given chemical compound. (The graphs in Fig. 2d correspond to the structure formula of acetylene $H—C≡C—H$.)

The study of the properties of a graph is facilitated if we take into consideration the following constants characterizing it.

Section 2. The Cyclomatic Number

In a generic graph with multiple lines let n be the number of points, m be the number of lines and p the number of connected components.

Given a graph with multiple lines G, the *cyclomatic number* is defined as the number

$$\nu(G) = m - n + p$$

It may be useful to consider separately, the expression

$$\rho(G) = n - p;$$

thus we have

$$\nu(G) = m - \rho(G).$$

To illustrate this definition let us examine the following example.

Figure 3 shows a graph with multiple lines; in our case we have

$$n = 8$$
$$m = 10$$
$$p = 2$$

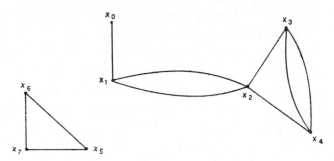

Fig. 3

and, hence, according to the definition

$$\rho(G) = 8 - 2 = 6; \quad \nu(G) = 10 - 6 = 4.$$

The properties of the cyclomatic number are specified by the following theorems:

FIRST THEOREM:

The cyclomatic number and the number $\rho(K)$ are non-negative.

Fig. 4a

Fig. 4b

In fact, consider a graph G consisting only of isolated points, similar to that in Fig. 4a (if there are n points the graph consists of n connected components).

Hence, we obviously have

$$\rho \ (G) = 0$$
$$\nu \ (G) = 0.$$

Let us now connect two points by means of a line (see Fig. 4b); the number of connected components decreases by one, hence

$$\rho(G) = 1.$$

Yet, the number of lines has increased by one, hence

$$\nu(G) = 1 - 1 = 0.$$

If we add another line (see Fig. 4c), the number of connected components decreases by one, and we have

$$\rho\ (G) = 2,$$

that is, $\rho(G)$ increases and, accordingly, the cyclomatic number does not change. In fact:

$$\nu(G) = 2 - 2 = 0.$$

It can occur, however, that by adding a new line the number of connected components is not affected (compare Fig. 4d with Fig. 4c); in this case $\rho(G)$ also does not vary, whereas the cyclomatic number increases by one.

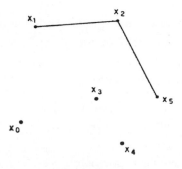

Fig. 4c

This reasoning is generally valid, that is, if there is an increase in $\rho(G)$, $\nu(G)$ does not change; if there is an increase in $\nu(G)$, $\rho(G)$ does not change. At any rate, the two numbers $\rho(G)$ and $\nu(G)$ cannot decrease and, hence, the statement is true.

If we keep in mind the definition of independent cycles (see page 16), the second property is characterized as follows:

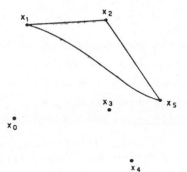

Fig. 4d

SECOND THEOREM:

The cyclomatic number of a graph with multiple lines equals the maximum number of independent cycles.

On the basis of the last remark in the demonstration of the preceding theorem, we can say that the cyclomatic number increases by one unit when the addition of a line enables us to consider new cycles of the graph.

Let μ_i, with $i = 1, 2, \ldots, r$, be linearly independent cycles, and r be their maximum number which can be found in a given graph. Let the addition of a line result in the appearance of s additional cycles

$$\mu'_k; \quad k = 1, 2, \ldots, s.$$

For example, cycle μ'_1, cannot be expressed linearly by means of cycles μ_i, hence cycles

$$\mu_1, \mu_2, \ldots, \mu_r, \mu'_1 \tag{1}$$

are linearly independent; on the other hand, it is easily established that the remaining cycles

$$\mu'_2, \mu'_3, \ldots, \mu'_s$$

can be expressed as linear combinations of the other cycles in $\mu_1, \mu_2, \ldots, \mu'_1$. Hence we conclude that if the cyclomatic number increases by one, the maximum number of independent cycles must also increase by one and, since this latter number equals zero when $\nu(G) = 0$, our asser-tion is true.

In particular, we infer that, if the cyclomatic number equals zero, the graph does not admit cycles, however it admits only one cycle, if the cyclomatic number equals one.

Section 3. The Chromatic Number

Let us mark the points on a graph by means of a certain number of various indices (for example, with various colors).

If for each point all the adjacent points are marked by p colors, we can say that the graph is a chromatic one of order p.

The minimum number whereby a graph becomes a chromatic one of order p, is called the *chromatic number* of the graph G and is indicated by the symbol $\gamma(G)$.

The chromatic number can be found by means of the following analytical method which relies upon the usual methods of linear programming. In order to determine whether the graph admits the number p as its chromatic order we proceed as follows:

We assume

$$\begin{cases} \xi_{iq} = 1 \text{ if point } x_i \text{ has the color } q \ (q = 1, 2, \ldots, p) \\ \xi_{iq} = 0 \text{ for the other cases} \end{cases}$$

$$\begin{cases} r_{ij} = 1 \text{ if line } u_j \text{ has an endpoint in } x_i \\ r_{ij} = 0 \text{ for the other cases} \end{cases}$$

and consider the following system of linear relationships

$$1a) \quad \sum_{q=1}^{p} \xi_{iq} = 1 \qquad i = 1, 2, \ldots, n$$

$$2a) \quad \sum_{k=1}^{n} r_{kj} \, \xi_{kq} \leqslant 1 \quad \begin{cases} j = 1, 2, \ldots, m \\ q = 1, 2, \ldots, p \end{cases}$$

(m denotes the number of lines with an endpoint in x_k). If the above system possesses solutions, then the reply to our question is in the affirmative.

In fact, the first system of n equations expresses the obvious fact that each point is associated with one color only.

The inequalities of the second system indicate that by fixing the particular color q and the particular point x_j joined with x_k by means of arc u_j, no more than one addend of the summation may be equal to one, all the other equalling zeros.

Since an addend equals zero if only one of the following three hypotheses is true, namely:

a) $r_{kj} = 0$; $\xi_{kq} = 0$, i.e., if x_k has not the color q and is not adjacent to x_j;

b) $r_{kj} = 0$; $\xi_{kq} = 1$, i.e., x_k has the color q but is not adjacent to x_j;

c) $r_{kj} = 1$; $\xi_{kq} = 0$, i.e., x_k has not the color q and is not adjacent to x_j;

it can be verified that the resulting inequality obtained by fixing q and j expresses the fact that any point contiguous to x_j must be colored differently from the latter.

We conclude that the chromatic number of the graph is p if it is the smallest number for which values of ξ_{ij} exist that are compatible with the system.

As already mentioned, the verification of the consistency of the linear equations constituting our system can be carried out by linear programming methods. It must be noted, however, that in this case the required solution must be limited to whole numbers (in particular 1 and 0).

Section 4. The Number of Internal Stability

In a given graph defined by the set X and correspondence T, we consider a proper sub-set of X; we have, for example, $S \subset X$.

In the case where any two of the points of S are not adjacent, we state that S is *internally stable*.

We can express the same fact by stating that the two sets TS and S have the empty set as an intersection.

Let us now consider the family of internally stable sets relative to graph G, and let $|S|$ be the number of elements of set S; we define the *number of internal stability* of graph G as the maximum of these numbers and designate it by $a(G)$.

For example, in the graph of Fig. 5, the number of internal stability is $a(G) = 3$. In fact, x_1, x_3, and x_5, taken in pairs, are not adjacent, whereas, if we add any other point, this is no longer true. On the other hand,

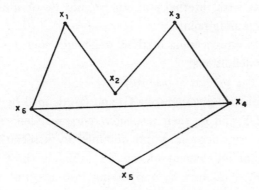

Fig. 5

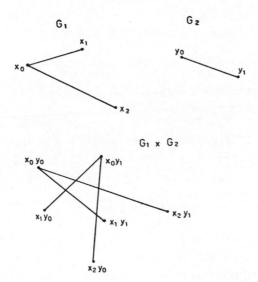

Fig. 6

sub-sets with internal stability cannot be obtained from the remaining points.

Before proceeding further, we should consider the following definitions:

(i) *The product of two graphs*

With two given graphs G_1 and G_2, defined by the sets X and Y and by their respective correspondences T_1 and T_2, we consider the graph obtained by associating with any point an element of set XY, which is the Cartesian product of X and Y, and taking into account the correspondence $T(x_i, y_j) = T_1(x_i) \times T_2(y_j)$; thus, by definition, we obtain the product graph $G_1 \times G_2$.

To obtain a clearer idea let us consider the two graphs indicated in Fig. 6.

In this case, the points of $X \times Y$ are

$$x_0 y_0; \quad x_0 y_1; \quad x_1 y_0; \quad x_1 y_1; \quad x_2 y_0; \quad x_2 y_1;$$

moreover, since $T_1(x_i)$ and $T_2(y_j)$ are given by

$T_1(x_i)$	$T_2(y_j)$
$Tx_0 = x_1$	$Ty_0 = y_1$
$Tx_1 = x_2$	$Ty_1 = y_0$
$Tx_2 = x_0$	

the correspondence $T(x_i; y_j)$ is

$T(x_0, y_0) = x_1 y_1;$	$T(x_1, y_1) = x_2 y_0$
$T(x_0, y_1) = x_1 y_0;$	$T(x_2, y_0) = x_0 y_1$
$T(x_1, y_0) = x_2 y_1;$	$T(x_2, y_1) = x_0 y_0$

and the product graph is that indicated in Fig. 6.

(ii) Conservative correspondence

When a uniform correspondence is applied to the elements of the set X, associated with a graph, the correspondence is called conservative if two points which are separate and nonadjacent correspond to two other points which conserve this property. For example, the correspondence

$$\begin{cases} X = x_1; \; x_2; \; x_3; \; x_4; \; x_5 \\ \sigma(x) = x_2; \; x_3; \; x_4; \; x_5; \; x_1 \end{cases}$$

applied to the graph shown in Fig. 7 possesses this conservation property.

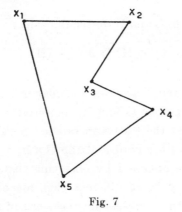

Fig. 7

We are now able to determine the main characteristics of the internal stability number; they are summarized in the following two sections.

Section 5. The Shannon Theorem

Theorem

If one of two given graphs G and H can be transformed into an internally stable set by means of a conservative correspondence σ, we have

$$a \, (G \times H) = a \, (G) \, a \, (H).$$

The theorem can be demonstrated with the aid of the following lemmas:

Lemma I

For two graphs G and H the relationship

$$a \, (G \times H) \geqslant a(G) \, a \, (H).$$

is true.

In fact, if S and T are two maximal internally stable sets relative to graphs G and H, respectively, we see im-immediately that the Cartesian product $S \times T$ is still internally stable with regard to graph $G \times H$.

This can be checked by observing that if (s_i, s_j); (t_i, t_j) are two pairs of different elements belonging to S and T, all of the corresponding elements of $S \times T$ are distinct $(s_i t_i \,; s_i t_j \,; s_j t_i \,; s_j t_j)$; moreover, the correspondence completing the definition of product graph $G \times H$ is such that all of the above points become nonadjacent (the above statement is convincing if we bear in mind that $s_i, s_j; t_i, t_j$ are not adjacent in S and T).

Thus we deduce that

$$a(G \times H) \geqslant |S \times T| = |S| \cdot |T| = a(G) \cdot a(H);$$

|A| indicates, as usual, the *cardinality* of the set A; that is, the number of elements of A.

The inequality sign indicates that the product $G \times H$ may yield the case that an internally stable set contains elements which do not belong to $S \times T$.

Lemma II

An internally stable set is transformed by means of the conservative correspondence σ into an internally stable set having the same number of elements.

In fact, correspondence σ is uniform by definition, hence, the elements of a set S cannot be fewer in number than the elements of $\sigma(S)$. But if S is internally stable and σ is conservative, the set $\sigma(S)$ remains internally stable and has the same cardinality as S. In fact, if $|\sigma(S)| < |S|$, one point of $\sigma(S)$ could correspond to two or more distinct points of S.

Lemma III

Let X be the set whence graph G is derived; if the application of a conservative correspondence to X determines an internally stable set $\sigma(X)$, the number of elements constituting the latter equals the internal stability number of graph G, that is

$$|\sigma(X)| = a(G).$$

In fact, if $\sigma(X)$ is internally stable it follows by definition

$$|\sigma(X)| \leqslant a(G). \tag{2}$$

On the other hand, $|\sigma(X)|$ cannot be less than $|\sigma(S_0)|$, where S_0 is a maximum internally stable set of G since $S_0 \subset X$ and, hence, by lemma II

$$|\sigma(X)| \geqslant |\sigma(S_0)| = |S_0| = a(G) \qquad (3)$$

From (2) and (3) we deduce the statement, namely

$$|\sigma(X)| = a(G).$$

We can now carry out the demonstration of the Shannon theorem in the following manner:

On the basis of Lemma I, according to which

$$a(G \times H) \geqslant a(G) \cdot a(H)$$

it is sufficient to show that, according to our hypothesis, the inequality sign cannot hold.

Let $\sigma(X)$ be an internally stable set obtained from set G by means of the conservative correspondence σ, and let us consider the sub-set of $G \times H$ as defined by the pairs $\{\sigma(X), y\}$ (where y is any element of H).

The correspondence which enables us to change from the elements of set $\{G \times H\}$ to the elements of $\{\sigma(X), y\}$ is conservative; let it be σ_0.

Then, if S_0 is a maximum internally stable set of $G \times H$ by lemma II the relationship

$$|\sigma_0(S_0)| = a(G \times H) = |S_0| \qquad (4)$$

is valid

Let us now number the elements of $\sigma_0(S_0)$ in the following fashion: first, we divide the set $\sigma_0(S_0)$ into several sub-sets, into each of which there fall the elements having as the first term of the pair the same element x_i. Then, by lemma II we can affirm that the number of these sub-sets is

$$|\sigma(X)| = a(G).$$

No more than $a(H)$ elements can fall into each of them since no two elements of $\sigma_0(S_0)$ are adjacent. Hence we conclude that

$$|\sigma_0(S_0)| \leqslant a(G) \cdot a(H).$$

Taking account of relationship (4) we can write

$$a(G \times H) \leqslant a(G) \cdot a(H)$$

whereas by lemma I an equality must be valid. This corresponds to our assertion.

Section 6. Relationship Between the Chromatic Number and the Internal Stability Number

Between the chromatic number and the internal stability number there exists the relationship

$$j(G)a(G) \geqslant n$$

where n represents the number of points in G.

In fact, it is possible to divide the set X into $j(G) = j$ internally stable sets consisting of points of the same color.

If $m_i \qquad i = 1,2,3, \ldots,$

is the number of elements constituting each of the above sets, we have $m_i \leqslant a(G)$ and, hence,

$$n = \sum_{i=1}^{\gamma} m_i \leqslant \gamma(G) \times a(G).$$

Section 7. An Example

We conclude by considering an important application.

In the information theory developed by Shannon there arises the following basic problem.

An information source can emit n individual signals; let x_i be any one of them, while y_i is the signal among n corresponding signals coming to a receiving station. If we assume that the emitted signals reach the receiving station without interferences, we can establish a uniform correspondence between the two sequences x_i and y_i, and the code adopted by the transmitting station cannot be the cause for misunderstandings at the receiving station.

In practice, however, there occur disturbances which distort the general signal emitted; hence, at the receiving station, it may be interpreted as another signal; on the other hand, when listening, a specific y_i is heard and there arises uncertainty as to whether the signal transmitted is the one actually picked up.

The effect of random noises can be studied by means of the law of conditional probability governing this phenomenon.

Precisely, if P $(A|B)$ is the probability that there occurs an event A subject to the occurrence of event B, to each broadcast of x_i we can apply the conditional law of probability P $(y_j|x_i)$ to various signals y_j received, and, conversely, to each reception of y_i we can apply the law of probability P $(x_j|y_i)$ determining which x_j has brought about the signal received.

In a situation like the one described above, we may be confronted with the problem of establishing the code to be adopted in order to avoid erroneous interpretations at the receiving station.

Let us mention a solution of the above problem obtained by utilizing the theory of graphs and by intentionally neglecting any probabilistic consideration which would lead us beyond the subject with which we intend to deal. Let us suppose that the transmission code consists of four seperate signals which, at the receiving end, may bring about a double interpretation (see Fig. 8).

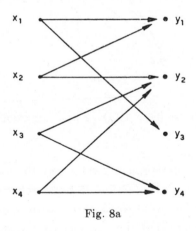

Fig. 8a

Figure 8a shows how the four signals x_i can be interpreted at the receiving station; Fig. 8b shows a graph where the points correspond to various signals emitted, and the signals which can be confused are connected by lines. The problem of finding a code consisting of signals with only one symbol, which would not result in misinterpretations, amounts to looking for a set with maximum internal stability in the graph thus obtained.

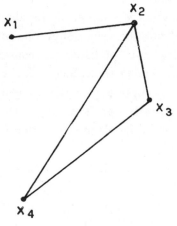

Fig. 8b

In our case we have $a(G) = 2$ and, for example,

$$S = \{x_1, x_3\}.$$

If we try to determine in which way the code becomes enriched by the introduction of two-symbol signals, we deduce from lemma I enunciated with regard to the Shannon theorem that the new code contains

$$a(G \times G) = a(G^2) \geqslant [a(G)]^2$$

different signals which cannot be confused. The Shannon

theorem determines under which conditions we should expect the new code to consist of exactly $[a(G)]^2$ signals.

Section 8. The External Stability Number

In a graph defined by a set X of points and a correspondence T, we say that a proper sub-set of X is *externally stable* if for each point belonging to its complement there exists an element which can be regarded as corresponding to that point by means of T.

We can write in symbols:

Given a $R \subset X$ such that if $r \epsilon R$, we have also $r \epsilon Tx$ for each $x \epsilon C_x(R)$, then R is externally stable.

If we consider all of the sets externally stable in a certain graph G, the *external stability number* is the least element of the set consisting of the numbers designating the elements in each of the externally stable sets. It is designated by $\beta(G)$.

Thus we have

$$\beta(G) = \min |R|$$

where $|R|$ is the cardinality of a generic externally stable sub-set R.

Section 9. Nucleus of a Graph

It may happen that in a graph G a proper sub-set of X is simultaneously externally and internally stable. In this case this sub-set is called the *nucleus* of the graph.

In a graph with the nucleus N the relationship

$$a(G) = \beta(G)$$

is true, that is, the external and internal stability numbers are identical.

In fact, from the definition of $a(G)$ and $\beta(G)$ we derive

$$a(G) \geqslant |N| \geqslant \beta(G)$$

Now, if M is the maximum internally stable set, and if we assume that $N \subset M$ there exists an element $m \in M$ which does not belong to N and is such that $Tm \cap N \neq 0$, since N is also externally stable; all the more it must be $Tm \cap M \neq 0$, hence M cannot be internally stable.

Likewise, if P is the minimum externally stable set, we assume that $N \supset P$; this implies the existence of a point $m \in M$, not belonging to P where $Tn \cap P \neq 0$, since P is externally stable. With all the more reason we should have $Tn \cap N \neq 0$, which is impossible since N is externally stable.

Section 10. Evaluation of the Fundamental Numbers of a Graph

In the case of graphs with a large number of points, the evaluation of the cyclomatic, chromatic, and internal and external stability numbers can be undertaken with the aid of appropriate algorithms which shall not be discussed here.

Readers interested in this subject are referred to original sources, for example, C. Berge, Theorie des Graphs et Ses Applications, published by Dunod.

Section 11. Associate and Incidence Matrices

In the case of certain problems which can be traced back to the theory of graphs it appears convenient to utilize the formal properties of matrices; this can be achieved by introducing the following definitions:

1) In a multiple graph G consisting of n points x_i, we consider the square matrix $A = ||a_{ij}||$ of the type $(n \times n)$ whose generic element a_{ij} represents the number of arcs connecting point x_i to point x_j.

A matrix thus defined is called a *matrix associated with graph* G. In particular, if the graph is simple, the associated matrix consists of elements equal to zero or one.

The example shown in Fig. 9 gives us a clearer idea of the above.

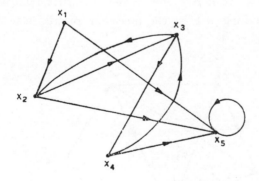

Fig. 9

The corresponding associated matrix is

$$\begin{Vmatrix} 0 & 1 & 0 & 0 & 1 \\ 0 & 0 & 1 & 0 & 1 \\ 0 & 1 & 0 & 1 & 0 \\ 0 & 0 & 1 & 0 & 1 \\ 0 & 0 & 0 & 0 & 1 \end{Vmatrix}$$

2) In a simple graph G consisting of n points x_i and m arcs u_j, we consider the rectangular matrix S of the type $(n \times m)$ whose elements s_{ij} equal $+1$, -1 and 0 according to whether x_i is, respectively, the initial point, the terminal point, or neither one of arc u_j

A matrix thus defined is called an *incidence matrix* relative to the arcs.

If the points of the graph are connected by lines and not by arcs, we derive the incidence matrix relative to lines by writing $+1$ in the preceding matrix instead of the elements -1.

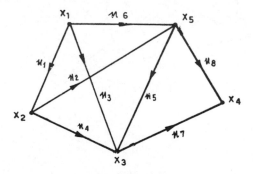

Fig. 10

As an example let us examine Fig. 10 which is a graph with $n = 5$ points and $m = 8$ arcs. The corresponding incidence matrix is

$$S = \begin{Vmatrix} 1 & 0 & 1 & 0 & 0 & 1 & 0 & 0 \\ -1 & 1 & 0 & 1 & 0 & 0 & 0 & 0 \\ 0 & 0 & -1 & -1 & -1 & 0 & 1 & 0 \\ 0 & 0 & 0 & 0 & 0 & 0 & -1 & -1 \\ 0 & -1 & 0 & 0 & 1 & -1 & 0 & 1 \end{Vmatrix}$$

Let us point out an interesting property of matrices associated with a graph:

Given two graphs G and G_1 having the same points, let us write

$$A = \|a_{ij}\| \text{ and } B = \|b_{ij}\|$$

for their associated matrices. It is possible to give an interesting interpretation to the product $A \times B$.

Let us note that the number of individual paths with length two, connecting point x_i to point x_j by means of pairs of arcs the first belonging to G and the second to G_1, is given by

$$\sum_{k=1}^{n} a_{ik} b_{kj}$$

We can recognize in this expression the typical element c_{ij} of the product matrix $C = A \cdot B$.

From this observation we can infer the following theorem (see Berge):

Let A be the matrix associated with a graph; the typical element d_{ij} of matrix $D = A^r$ (A to the rth power) represents the number of different courses of length r connecting point x_i to point x_j.

To corroborate what was stated above let us assume that the theorem is true for the value $(r-1)$; it will also be true for the value r on the strength of what was stated above. It is sufficient to note that in our case b_{ij} may be considered as the number of different courses connecting x_i to x_j in a graph derived from the assigned one by introducing as many arcs $(x_i x_j)$ as there are different courses of length $r-1$ which connect the above points in the original graph.

On the other hand, the theorem is true for $r=2$; hence, it is true for any r.

Section 12. Trees and Tree Derivations

1. We have already said that a graph is called a "tree" if it is finite, connected, without cycles and consists of at least two points.

Of the various characteristics of these particular types of graphs let us recall only the following one.

In a given graph without loops and with n points we consider the square matrix $B(n \times n) = ||b_{ij}||$ whose elements are defined in the following fashion:

$$b_{ij} = \begin{cases} |Tx_i| & \text{if } i=j \\ -1 & \text{if there exists an edge } (x_i x_j) \\ 0 & \text{if } (x_i x_j) \text{ does not exist } (i \neq j) \end{cases} \tag{5}$$

Then, the following theorem (see Trent) is true:

The number of individual trees with n points which are partial graphs of the one assigned, equals one of the minors relative to any diagonal element derived from the square matrix B.

To prove the above let us, in the first place, point out that if in graph G, after having assigned an arbitrary direction to the lines, we consider the incidence matrix S relative to the arcs, the general term of the product matrix $V = S \cdot S'$.

S' being the transpose of S,

$$v_{ij} = \sum_{k=1}^{n} s_{ik} s'_{kj}$$

coincides with b_{ij}. This is checked quite easily by taking into account the definition of S. In fact, if $i = j$, we have

$$v_{ii} = \sum_{k=1}^{n} s_{ik} s'_{ki} = \sum_{k=1}^{n} s^2_{ik}$$

that is, v_{ii} equals the sum of as many units as there are non-zero elements on the i-th line of matrix S; but each line X having x_i as an end point corresponds to a non-zero element, hence $v_{ii} = |Tx_i|$.

Instead, if $i \neq j$, the following two cases may be encountered;

a) The line segment $(x_i x_j)$ does not exist, hence $v_{ij} = 0$ since the elements s_{ik} and s'_{kj} cannot both be different from zero (remember that $s_{ik} \neq 0$ if x_i is an endpoint of u_k and $s'_{kj} \neq 0$ if u_k has x_j as an endpoint).

b) The line segment $(x_i x_j)$ does exist, hence $v_{ij} = -1$ insofar as s_{ik} and s'_{kj} are both different from zero and of opposite signs, as can be ascertained by repeating the reasoning used above in a).

Following is an example:

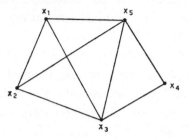

Fig. 11a

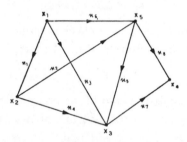

Fig. 11b

Let us examine the graph shown in Fig. 11a and let us give a direction to its arcs as shown in Fig. 11b. The incidence matrix S is

$$
S = \begin{Vmatrix}
1 & 0 & 1 & 0 & 0 & 1 & 0 & 0 \\
-1 & 1 & 0 & 1 & 0 & 0 & 0 & 0 \\
0 & 0 & -1 & -1 & -1 & 0 & 1 & 0 \\
0 & 0 & 0 & 0 & 0 & 0 & -1 & -1 \\
0 & -1 & 0 & 0 & 1 & -1 & 0 & 1
\end{Vmatrix}
$$

and, hence,

$$S \cdot \widetilde{S} = \begin{Vmatrix} 3 & -1 & -1 & 0 & -1 \\ -1 & 3 & -1 & 0 & -1 \\ -1 & -1 & 4 & -1 & -1 \\ 0 & 0 & -1 & 2 & -1 \\ 1 & -1 & -1 & -1 & 4 \end{Vmatrix}$$

which coincides with matrix B, which is evident from Fig. 11a.

If we consider in B, for example, the minor Δ_1 of b_{11}, we have

$$\Delta_1 = \begin{vmatrix} 3 & -1 & 0 & -1 \\ -1 & 4 & -1 & -1 \\ 0 & -1 & 2 & -1 \\ -1 & -1 & -1 & 4 \end{vmatrix} = 40.$$

This means that from the graph under consideration we can derive 40 trees constituted by 5 points.

Let us now note that a tree with n points consists of $n-1$ lines; moreover, if we want to derive a tree from a graph G of the order n, utilizing all the points, we must take into account all the possible sub-sets I belonging to set M of the lines of the graph, such as $|I| = n-1$, and have to ascertain that the conditions defining a tree are satisfied.

Finding a tree among the partial graphs derived in the above fashion is facilitated by the following theorem (see D. König):

Given the incidence matrix S, relative to a connected graph, the jth row is eliminated, and the new matrix so obtained is denoted by N.

The minors of greatest order able to be extracted from N are equal to ± 1, if the lines of the graph associated with them determine a tree, are zero otherwise.

To avoid a direct calculation of these non-zero determinants, which is frequently laborious, we observe that Det $(N \cdot N')$ is expressible in the form of the sum of the squares of all the above-mentioned minors. Such a sum is necessarily equal to the number of trees which can be derived from the graph.

To verify this, let us recall the Binet-Cauchy formula by means of which the determinant of the product of two matrices $A(k \times m)$ and $B(m \times k)$ can be expressed as the sum of the products of all the minors of order k derived from A by the corresponding minors of the same order obtained from B, $(k \leqslant m)$.

In symbols

$$\mathrm{Det}(A \cdot B) = \mathrm{Det}(AK_I) \cdot \mathrm{Det}(B_I K)$$

where K represents the set of the first k natural and I is any subset of k elements of the set of the first m natural numbers.

If we put $A = N$ and $B = N'$, we have

$$\Delta_i = \mathrm{Det}(B_{KK}) = \mathrm{Det}(S_{KM} \widetilde{S}_{MK}) = \underset{\substack{I \subset M \\ |I|=n-1}}{\Sigma} \{\mathrm{Det}(S_{KI})\}^2 \tag{6}$$

But if the jth row of S has been eliminated, $\mathrm{Det}(N \cdot N')$ is the minor of b_{jj} in B, and the theorem of Treat is proved.

2. From the point x_1 of a tree we replace each line by an arc so that x_1 is the initial point of the first arc and any other point is the terminal point of any other arc.

A graph thus defined is called "arborescence" (tree derivation) and x_1 is its root.

Let us now consider a directed graph G consisting by n points, and let $A = ||a_{ij}||$ be its associated matrix, D be a diagonal matrix whose generic element d_{ii} represents the number of arcs intersecting at point x_i.

The difference matrix $D - A$ is given by

$$D - A = \begin{Vmatrix} \sum_{i=j=1} a_{i1} & -a_{12} \dots -a_{1n} \\ -a_{21} & \sum_{i=j=2} a_{i2} \dots -a_{2n} \\ \cdot & \cdot \quad \cdot \quad \cdot \quad \cdot \quad \cdot \quad \cdot \\ \cdot & \cdot \quad \cdot \quad \cdot \quad \cdot \quad \cdot \quad \cdot \\ -a_{n1} & \dots \dots \dots \sum_{i=j=n} a_{in} \end{Vmatrix}$$

and let Δ_1 be the minor obtained from the determinant by eliminating the first row and the first column.

Let us now consider the following theorem which is similar to the last theorem of the preceding paragraph:

A necessary and sufficient condition for a graph G without loops having $n-1$ arcs to be an "arborescence" with the root x_1 is that $\Delta_1 = 1$. In all the other cases $\Delta_1 = 0$.

For the demonstration of the above, see Lemma IV and V of the following section, and take into account that matrix $D - A$ is a particular case of $D - C$ defined below.

Section 13. A Theorem Relating to "Arborescences"

Let us associate a directed graph G without loops with a function of its arcs; if $c(x_i x_j)$ is its generic value we can, accordingly, form a square matrix $C = ||c_{ij}||$ where $c_{ij} = c(x_i x_j)$. Let us then consider the diagonal matrix $D = ||d_{ij}||$ where

$$d_{ii} = \sum_{k \neq i} c_{ki}$$

(c_{ii} is zero).

Finally, let us form the determinant

$$\Delta = \text{Det}(D - C).$$

Let H be the set of points defining an "arborescence₁" extracted from G, having its root in x_1, and let

$$c(H) = \Pi_{\substack{x_i \text{ and } x_j \in H}} c_{ij}.$$

where Π means the product.

We intend to prove the following theorem:[1]

The minor Δ_1 of determinant Δ equals the sum of $c(H)$ relative to all of the "arborescences" extracted from G with roots in x_1, that is,

$$\Delta_1 = \sum_{H \subset G} c(H).$$

We note in the first place that the elements of Δ_1, which we indicate by b_{ij} are given by

$$b_{ij} = -c_{ij} \qquad\qquad i, j = 2, 3, \ldots n; \; i \neq j \qquad (7)$$

---

[1]Developed by Bott and Mayberry, *Matrices and Trees*, see References.

$$b_{jj} = \sum_{\substack{i=1 \\ i \neq j}}^{n} c_{ij} \qquad\qquad j = 2,3, \ldots n \qquad\qquad (8)$$

From the first we obtain

$$\sum_{i \neq j}^{n} b_{ij} = -\sum_{i \neq j}^{n} c_{ij};$$

by summing this with (8)

$$\sum_{i=2}^{n} b_{ij} = c_{1j} \qquad\qquad (9)$$

This suggests the possibility of establishing a one-to-one correspondence between a graph and a matrix; in fact, the definition of b_{ij} enables us to change from a certain graph G to a matrix B, while equations (7) and (9) show us how to plot the graph G when the elements of Δ_1 are known.

The demonstration of the theorem is based on the following lemmas:

LEMMA I

$\sum_{H \subset G} c(H)$ and Δ_1 are multilinear forms of the values of c_{ij}.

For $\sum_{H \subset G} c(H)$ this statement is obvious; for Δ_1 it should be noted that each term of the development of the determinant is of the type

$$\Pi_{k=2}^{n} b_{i_K} K.$$

On the other hand, $b_{i_K} K$ is a linear combination of

$$c_{ij} \quad ; \qquad i = 1, \ldots, n; \qquad i \neq j$$

and, hence, c_{ij} cannot appear twice in each term of the expansion.

Lemma II

If in G there is a point x_k distinct from the root, which is not a terminal point of any arc, then

$$\Delta_1 = \sum_{H \subset G} c(H) = 0$$

In fact, according to our hypothesis x_k is not connected with the root and consequently $\sum c(H) = 0$ since each addend equals zero.

Moreover, each term in the expansion of the determinant contains a factor equalling zero: that term in which $c_{ik} = 0$ appears; whence we derive $\Delta_1 = 0$.

Lemma III

If the graph is constituted by two disconnected graphs G_1 and G_2, we have

$$\Delta_1 = \sum_{H \subset G} c(H) = 0.$$

The statement that $\sum_{H \subset G} c$ (H) = 0 is obvious.

In order to establish that also $\Delta_1 = 0$, it is sufficient to show that the system of linear homogeneous equations having as determinant Δ_1, admits of a solution consisting of values which are not all zero (let us bear in mind the condition ensuring the existence of solutions different from zero in a linear homogeneous system of n equations and n unknowns).

The system

$$-\sum_{\substack{i=2 \\ i \neq j}}^{n} c_{ij} y_i + \sum_{\substack{i=1 \\ i \neq j}}^{n} c_{ij} y_j = 0 \quad j = 2, 3, \ldots, n$$

can be written as

$$\sum_{i=1}^{n} c_{ij}(y_i - y_j) = 0 \qquad j = 2, 3, \ldots, n$$

if $y_1 = 0$.

Then we see that

$$\begin{cases} y_i = 0 \text{ when } x_i \subset G_1 \\ y_i = 1 \text{ when } x_i \subset G_2 \end{cases}$$

constitute a solution not equalling zero for the system (it should be borne in mind that if we assume $x_i \subset G_1$ and $x_j \subset G_2$ then $c_{ij} = 0$).

Lemma IV

If the graph contains exactly $n-1$ arcs and is not an "arborescence", then

$$\Delta_1 = \sum_{H \subset G} c(H).$$

In fact, in this case either hypothesis of lemma II or that of lemma III is valid.

Lemma V

If the graph belongs to an "arborescence", then

$$\Delta_1 = \sum_{H \subset G} c(H).$$

Let us assume that the indices characterizing the points in the graph have been ordered in such a way that if $(x_i x_j)$ is an arc, $j > i$.

Then we find that

$$b_{jj} = c\,(x_i x_j)$$

$b_{ij} = 0$ if $i > j$ or if x_i is not the intial point of $(x_i x_j)$.

Hence we derive that

$$\Delta_1 = \prod_{j=2}^{n} b_{jj} = \prod_{\substack{x_i \,\varepsilon\, X' \\ x_j \,\varepsilon\, 'IX}} c(x_i,\ x_j) \text{ with } X' \subseteq X.$$

On the other hand, if $X' = X$, then we have

$$\Delta_1 = c(\mathrm{H})$$

if $X' \subset X$

$$\Delta_1 = 0 = c(\mathrm{H}).$$

Thereupon we proceed to the demonstration by noting that the necessary and sufficient condition for the two multilinear forms of the n-th order with the same variables to be identical is that they assume identical values when all the variables are different from zero.

But Δ_1 and $\sum_{\mathrm{H} \subset \mathrm{G}} c(\mathrm{H})$ are, on the basis of Lemma I, two multilinear forms of the nth order, hence Lemma IV and Lemma V hold and the theorem is true.

Section 14. A Particular Case

There arises an interesting special case when we assume that

$$c(x_i x_j) \begin{cases} = 1 \text{ if the arc } (x_i x_j) \text{ exists} \\ = 0 \text{ if this arc does not exist.} \end{cases}$$

With such an assumption we have $c(\mathrm{H}) = 1$ and Δ_1 equals the number of "arborescences" which can be extracted from the graph. Hence we can state the following significant *corollary* (by Tutte and Bott):

If G is a graph without loops, with associated matrix A, the number of "arborescences" with root x_1 which can be extracted from G equals the value of Δ_1. Let us show by means of an example what has been stated above.

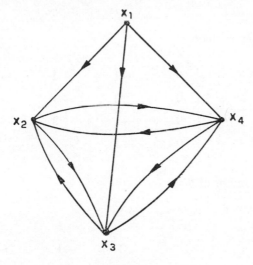

Fig. 12

The matrix associated with the graph shown in Fig. 12 is

$$A = \begin{Vmatrix} 0 & 1 & 1 & 1 \\ 0 & 0 & 1 & 1 \\ 0 & 1 & 0 & 1 \\ 0 & 1 & 1 & 0 \end{Vmatrix}$$

According to definition, the diagonal matrix D is

$$
D = \begin{Vmatrix}
0 & 0 & 0 & 0 \\
0 & 3 & 0 & 0 \\
0 & 0 & 3 & 0 \\
0 & 0 & 0 & 3
\end{Vmatrix}
$$

Hence we have

$$
B = D - A = \begin{Vmatrix}
0 & -1 & -1 & -1 \\
0 & 3 & -1 & -1 \\
0 & -1 & 3 & -1 \\
0 & -1 & -1 & 3
\end{Vmatrix}
$$

and the minor of b_{11} is

$$
\varDelta_1 = \begin{Vmatrix}
3 & -1 & -1 \\
-1 & 3 & -1 \\
-1 & -1 & 3
\end{Vmatrix} = 16
$$

This means that from the graph considered, there can be extracted 16 "arborescences"; they are shown in Fig. 13 (the numbers appearing near the arcs will be used in subsequent considerations).

Let us now assume that with the various arcs of the graph there are associated the values of the functions c_{ij} in the fashion shown in Fig. 14.

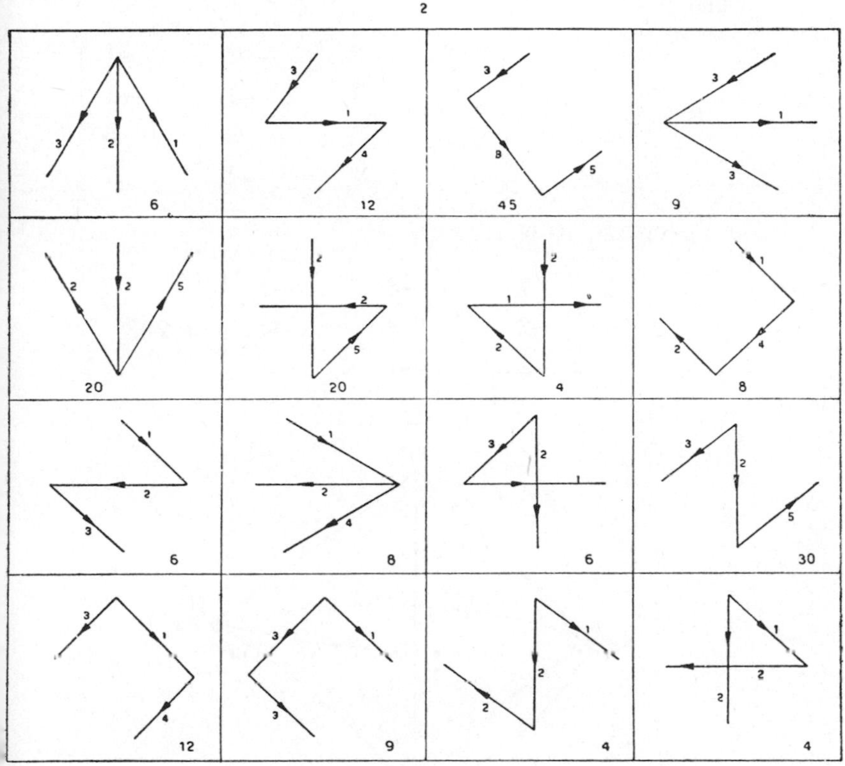

Fig. 13

The associated matrix C and the diagonal matrix are

$$
C = \left\| \begin{array}{cccc}
0 & 3 & 2 & 1 \\
0 & 0 & 3 & 1 \\
0 & 2 & 0 & 5 \\
0 & 2 & 4 & 0
\end{array} \right\| ; \quad
D = \left\| \begin{array}{cccc}
0 & 0 & 0 & 0 \\
0 & 7 & 0 & 0 \\
0 & 0 & 9 & 0 \\
0 & 0 & 0 & 7
\end{array} \right\|
$$

whence

$$B = D - C = \begin{Vmatrix} 0 & -3 & -2 & -1 \\ 0 & 7 & -3 & -1 \\ 0 & -2 & 9 & -5 \\ 0 & -2 & -4 & 7 \end{Vmatrix}$$

and the minor Δ_1 is

$$\Delta_1 = \begin{Vmatrix} 7 & -3 & -1 \\ -2 & 9 & -5 \\ -2 & -4 & 7 \end{Vmatrix} = 203.$$

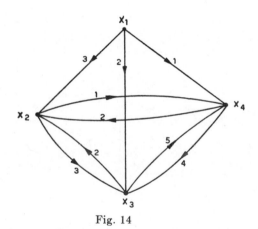

Fig. 14

Let us consider the products $c(H)$ shown in the diagram; by summing them we obtain precisely 203, which is in complete accordance with the theorem described.

CHAPTER III

Transport Networks

Section 1. Introduction

After having set forth the basic concepts relating to the general theory of graphs, we are going to investigate a special type of graph called a transport network; the study of its properties will enable us to find the solution to the economic problems described at the beginning of this book.

The definition of a transport network has already been given on page 16; the reader will recall that a graph can be considered a network when it is possible to define an initial point x_0 (a point which is the extreme of arcs which are all directed from it) and a terminal point z (a point which is the extreme of arcs which are all directed towards it) and each arc of the graph has been associated with a number $c(u) \geqslant 0$ which is called capacity of the arc u.

Section 2. The Flow

An idea closely associated with the concept of a transport network is that of *flow*. It can be defined in the following way:

a) On a set of arcs u constituting the network we define a function with integer, non-negative values.

b) Let the following sequence of conditions be true for its values:

$$\varphi(u_i) \leqslant c(u_i) \qquad i = 1, 2, \ldots$$

c) for each point x_i of the network different from the initial and terminal points, we have

$$\sum_{u = \overrightarrow{x_k x_i}} \varphi(u) - \varphi \sum_{u = \overrightarrow{x_i x_k}} (u) = 0$$

(some authors call this the *conservation condition* inasmuch as it is equivalent to saying that at any intermediate point, flows are neither created nor destroyed).

Each function $\varphi(u)$ thus determined is a flow with respect to the network under consideration.

Owing to property c), the sum of the values for $\varphi(u)$ relative to the arcs originating from the network initial point, equals the sum of the values for $\varphi(u)$ associated with arcs terminating at the initial point. Hence we have

$$\sum_{u = \overrightarrow{x_0 x_k}} \varphi(u) = \sum_{u = \overrightarrow{x_k z}} \varphi(u) = \Phi$$

The number Φ thus defined is called *value of the flow*.

Section 3. Section of a Graph

Definition

In a given transport network suppose that the set of points is divided into two sub-sets (obviously complementary) P and C_u (P) in such a way that one of them contains the initial and the other the terminal point of the network; thus we say that a *cut* has been applied to the network.

Let us now consider the sum of the capacities of arcs connecting the points of one of the sub-sets to the points of the other one; this sum will be called *cut value* and designated by the symbol Γ [1].

As a rule, with varying sections the value of Γ varies as well, but this occurs in such a fashion that there exists the relationship

$$\Phi \leqslant \Gamma \qquad (10)$$

In fact, as we have seen

$$\Phi = \sum_{j=1}^{n} \varphi(x_0 x_j)$$

and by adding the quantity

$$\sum_{i \varepsilon (P-x_0)} \sum_{j=1}^{n} [\varphi(x_i x_j) - \varphi(x_j x_i)],$$

which equals zero owing to the property c) of the preceding section, we obtain

$$\Phi = \sum_{j=1}^{n} \varphi(x_0 x_j) + \sum_{i \varepsilon(P-x_0)} \sum_{j=1}^{n} [\varphi(x_i x_j) - \varphi(x_j x_i)] =$$

$$= \sum_{i \varepsilon P} \sum_{j=1}^{n} [\varphi(x_i x_j) - \varphi(x_j x_i)] = \sum_{i \varepsilon P} \sum_{i \varepsilon P} [\varphi(x_i x_j) - \varphi(x_j x_i)] +$$

$$+ \sum_{i \varepsilon P} \sum_{j \varepsilon C_x(P)} [\varphi(x_i x_j) - \varphi(x_j x_i)]$$

---

[1] We shall frequently use the more explicit symbol $\Gamma[Y, C(Y)]$ which specifies the complementary sub-sets defining the section.

where the first addend equals zero because $\varphi(x_i x_j)$ and $\varphi(x_j x_i)$ cancel each other in pairs; hence we can write

$$\Phi = \sum_{i \varepsilon P} \sum_{j \varepsilon C_x(P)} [\varphi(x_i\, x_j) - \varphi(x_j\, x_i)] \leq \sum_{i \varepsilon P} \sum_{j \varepsilon C_x(P)} c(x_i\, x_j) =$$
$$= \Gamma[P, C_x(P)]$$

Let us point out that if in (1) the equality sign holds, the corresponding values for the flow and the cut are, respectively, the highest and the lowest values permissible in the graph.   In fact, considering the maximum among the possible values for Φ, Γ cannot assume lower values and, on the other hand, Φ may not exceed the smallest of the values for Γ.

We may wonder at this point whether the relationship

$$\Phi_{\max} = \Gamma_{\min}$$

(where $\Phi_{\max}$ is the maximum flow and $\Gamma_{\min}$ the minimum cut) is valid for any graph.   Let us note that on the basis of what was discussed we can only affirm that in the case of equality the values for Φ and Γ are extreme values; we cannot infer that if we consider the maximum for Φ and the minimum for Γ these will always be equal.

The answer to the foregoing question is given by the following theorem.

Section 4. The Ford and Fulkerson Theorem [1]

In any transport network, maximum flow equals minimum capacity of a cut.

---

[1] L. R. Ford, D. R. Fulkerson, *Maximal Flow through a Network*, Canadian Journ. of Math., 8, 1956.

We prove the theorem ([1]) by showing that in any graph it is always possible to determine a cut whose value equals that of maximum flow; on the basis of preceding considerations this is equivalent to having proved the theorem.

Let us consider all the possible paths originating from x_0 satisfying the inequality

$$\varphi^*(x_i x_j) - \varphi^*(x_j x_i) < c(x_i x_j)$$

where the asterisk indicates that they are the values of maximum flow.

If x_k is the last point of any path, then certainly $x_k \neq z$; if this were not the case, we would have a path connecting x_0 to z along which the flow could be increased and hence the value of the flow under consideration would not be a maximum.

We can affirm that the set P of points belonging to the paths considered defines, together with its complementary $C_x(P)$, a section of the graph.

If, per absurdum, we had

$$\Phi_{max} < \Gamma[P, C_x(P)]$$

that is,

$$\underset{i \varepsilon P}{\Sigma} \underset{j \varepsilon C_x(P)}{\Sigma} [\varphi^*(x_i x_j) - \varphi^*(x_j x_i)] < \underset{i \varepsilon P}{\Sigma} \underset{j \varepsilon C_x(P)}{\Sigma} c(x_i x_j)$$

---

[1]Here we follow a proof developed by D. Gale: David Gale, *A Theorem on Flows in Networks*, Pacific J. of Mathematics, Vol. 7 (1957).

there would exist at least two points, x_k belonging to P and x_l belonginging to $C_x(P)$, where

$$\varphi^*(x_k x_l) - \varphi^*(x_l x_k) < c(x_k x_l)$$

whence x_l should belong to P, which contradicts our hypothesis.

Section 5. Determination of Maximum Flow

A problem of considerable importance for transport networks consists in determining the function $\varphi(u)$ so as to maximize for a given network the value Φ of the flow, and this irrespective of the theoretical interest of the Ford and Fulkerson theorem.

Efficient research of maximum flow can be facilitated by using an algorithm, suggested by the above authors, and whose application leads also to proving the theorem.

At first we note that if

$$\varphi(u) = c(u)$$

arc u is called *saturated*; in addition a given flow is said to be *complete* if any line leading from x_0 to z contains at least one saturated arc. We will show that proceeding from any incomplete flow, we can easily obtain a complete one; if a complete flow is given, we can, with a finite number of iterations, derive a flow with maximum values.

To this end let us point out that if a given initial flow is incomplete, it is possible to determine a path which connects x_0 with z where no arc is saturated; in this case we should add to the various values of $\varphi(u)$ relative to the arcs of such a path the smallest element of the successive differences $c(u) - \varphi(u)$.

Thus, the line under consideration contains at least one saturated arc.

If we proceed in similar manner with the other paths of the same type, we obtain a complete flow.

At this stage let us mark the initial point by the index 0 (zero) and let us investigate the adjacent set of points; each of them is marked by 0. If x_i is one of these points, the adjacent non-marked points should be considered; let x_j be one of these points and let us mark it by $+i$ if

$$\varphi(x_i x_j) < c(x_i x_j) \quad \text{and the arc is } x_i \to x_j,$$

and by $-i$ if

$$\varphi(x_i x_j) < 0 \quad \text{because the arc is } x_j \to x_i.$$

The arcs for which equality rather than inequality is valid must not be marked.

As a rule, adopting this procedure, only some points of the network will be marked; thus, it can occur that at the end of this procedure point z is marked; this fact means that it is possible to look for a path between x_0 and z having points marked by the indices of the preceding points and non-saturated arcs running in a negative direction.

Let us modify the flow relative to the arcs of such a path by adding to each term $\varphi(u)$, relative to arcs running in the same sense as the path, the minimum element (designated by m) of the sequence of values

$$c(x_i x_j) - \varphi(x_i x_j); \; \varphi(x_j x_i)$$

and subtracting the same quantity from the terms $\varphi(u)$ relative to arcs running in a sense opposite to that of the path.

Thus we obtain a new flow function whose value is increased by the quantity m. In fact, we can be sure that in one of the arcs whose final extreme is the terminal point, the flow has increased by m.

This procedure has to be repeated as many times as it is necessary to arrive at a stage where point z can no longer be marked.

This fact indicates that we have attained the maximum value of flow Φ permitted by the transport network under consideration.

In fact, if A is the set of points which have not been marked, because x_0 does not belong to A while z does belong to A, A and $C_n(A)$ define a cut, and therefore we have

$$\Phi = \sum_{i \varepsilon A} \varphi(x_k \, x_i) - \sum_{i \varepsilon A} \varphi(x_i \, x_k) = \sum_{i \varepsilon A} c(x_k \, x_i) =$$

$$= \Gamma[A, C_u(A)].$$

As we have already seen, the equality sign assures that Φ takes on the maximum permissible value and $\Gamma[A, C_n(A)]$ takes on the minimum permissible value.

It is obvious that if for a complete initial flow point z cannot be reached by the marking process, this initial flow is a maximum.

Thus we have shown a practical procedure for the determination of maximum flow and at the same time corroborated the Ford and Fulkerson theorem.

Section 6. A Numerical Example

Let us now consider a numerical example which will help the reader grasp the method.

Examine the transport network shown in Fig. 15; here are shown the directions of the arcs; the capacity of each arc has also been indicated.

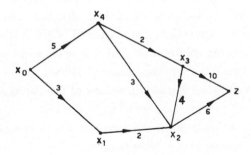

Fig 15

In order to make sure that the flow considered originally can be achieved, one adopts a sequence of $\varphi(u)$ consisting of zero values and proceeds as indicated in the following table.

Archi	Φ'	Φ''	Φ'''	Φ''''
$x_0 \; x_4$	0	2	$\bar{5}$	$\bar{5}$
$x_0 \; x_1$	0	0	0	2
$x_4 \; x_3$	0	$\bar{2}$	$\bar{2}$	$\bar{2}$
$x_4 \; x_2$	0	0	$\bar{3}$	$\bar{3}$
$x_1 \; x_2$	0	0	0	$\bar{2}$
$x_1 \; z$	0	0	3	5
$x_2 \; x_3$	0	0	0	0
$x_3 \; z$	0	2	2	2

The first column shows the various arcs making up the network written in the order of their direction; the second column shows the values (zero values) of the initial flow; in the following columns we find flow values obtained by various iterations in the manner shown below. The marked values are saturation values of the corresponding arcs.

In the third column we consider course $x_0x_4x_3z$, and arc x_4x_3 saturated by increasing the flow as much as possible, that is, by 2.

The fourth column gives data regarding course $x_0x_4x_2z$ with an increase of 3. In this case there is a saturation also of the terminal arc x_0x_4 and, hence, it is useless to consider other lines containing this arc.

The fifth column contains data concerning course $x_0x_1x_2z$ and a flow increased by 2.

We can readily be convinced that once complete flow has been obtained, it is impossible, in our case, to increase the flow by considering courses containing arcs running in the opposite direction.

Thus we conclude that maximum flow is $\Phi = 7$ (this can be read from the arcs originating from x_0 or converging in z).

Section 7. The Gale Theorem([1])

We shall now describe the following theorem developed by D. Gale([2]), in view of its applications to our argument.

In order to be more explicit some preliminary considerations are stated: in a given transport network G defined by the set N of its points and the capacities of its arcs, one has to define by means of the points of the given graph a real function $d(x_i)$, to be called "demand". It is expedient to introduce the following specification: if $d(x) \geqslant 0$, we are dealing with proper demand, while if $d(x_i) < 0$, it is preferable to speak of "offer".

We say that a demand can be achieved if for each x_j belonging to the graph the relationship

$$\sum_{x_i \in N} \varphi(x_i, x_j) \geqslant d(x_j)$$

is true, that is, if there exists such a flow that the algebraic

---

[1] In the Anglo-Saxon literature Gale's theorem is also called "Feasibility Theorem".

[2] D. Gale, *A Theorem on Flows in Networks*, Pacific Jour. of Math., 7, 1957.

sum of its values relative to arcs having a terminal point in x_j is not smaller than the demand in x_j.

THEOREM

The necessary and sufficient conditions, in order that demand $D(x_j)$ be achieved, are that for each set S of points of the graph the following relationship be true:

$$\sum_{x_i \varepsilon S'} d(x_j) \le \sum_{x_j \varepsilon S; x_j \varepsilon S'} c(x_1, x_j)$$

where $S' = C_N(S)$, and $c(x_i x_j)$ is the associated capacity of an arc $(x_i x_j)$.

This condition is necessary.   In fact, if $d(x_i)$ is achievable, there exists by definition a flow $\varphi(x_i x_j)$ such that

$$\sum_{x_j \varepsilon S'} d(x_j) \le \sum_{x_i \varepsilon N; x_j \varepsilon S'} \varphi(x_1, x_j) =$$

$$= \sum_{x_i \varepsilon S; x_j \varepsilon S'} \varphi(x_1, x_j) + \sum_{x_i e x_j \varepsilon S'} \varphi(x_1, x_j).$$

Taking into account that

$$\sum_{x_i e x_j \varepsilon S'} \varphi(x_i x_j) = 0$$

we have

$$\sum_{x_j \varepsilon S'} d(x_j) \le \sum_{x_i \varepsilon S; x_j \varepsilon S'} \varphi(x_1, x_j) \le \sum_{x_i \varepsilon S; x_j \varepsilon S'} c(x_1, x_j).$$

This corresponds to our assertion.

The condition is sufficient.   We have to prove that if

$$\sum_{x_j \varepsilon S} d(x_j) - \sum_{x_i \varepsilon S; x_j \varepsilon S'} c(x_i, x_j) \le 0 \tag{10}$$

there exists a flow such that

$$\sum_{x_i \, \varepsilon \, N} \varphi(x_i , x_j) \geq d(x_j) \qquad \text{per } x_j \, \varepsilon \, N \qquad (11)$$

With the aid of a definition of an appropriate graph $\overline{G}$ derived from G we shall show that the first term of (10) is equal to the difference between the capacities of two cuts applied to graph $\overline{G}$; then, availing ourselves of the Ford and Fulkerson theorem, we shall show that bringing the flow of $\overline{G}$ to a maximum implies the fulfillment of condition (11).

Let us therefore consider a new graph $\overline{G}$ made up of points of G and by two additional points which we denote by x_0 and x_{n+1} and consider them as initial and terminal points, respectively, of the graph; moreover, let U be the set of points of G for which $d(x_i) \leqslant 0$. The capacities $\bar{c}(x_i x_j)$ associated with the arcs of $\overline{G}$ are defined as follows:

$\bar{c}(x_i x_j) = c(x_i, x_j)$ if x_i and x_j belong to G.
$\bar{c}(x_0, x_j) = -d(x_j)$ if x_j belongs to U. $\qquad (12)$
$\bar{c}(x_i, x_{n+1}) = d(x_i)$ if x_i belongs to $U' = C_N(U)$
$\bar{c}(x_i, x_j) = 0$ in all the other cases

After having introduced these positions we first wish to show that the cut $(\overline{N} - x_{n+1}, x_{n+1})$, (where $\overline{N}$ is the set of the points of $\overline{G}$) applied to graph $\overline{G}$ is a minimum. In fact, if (S and S') is any cut in $\overline{G}$, where

$$S = \overline{S} - x_0; \quad S' = \overline{S}' - x_{n+1}$$

we have, according to definitions (12)

$$\sum_{x_i \,\varepsilon\, \overline{s}\,;\, x_j \,\varepsilon\, \overline{s}'} \bar{c}(x_i,\, x_j) = \sum_{x_i \,\varepsilon\, s\,;\, x_j \,\varepsilon\, s'} \bar{c}(x_i,\, x_j) + \sum_{x_j \,\varepsilon\, s'} \bar{c}(x_0,\, x_j) +$$

$$\sum_{x_i \,\varepsilon\, s} \bar{c}(x_i,\, x_{n+1}) + \bar{c}(x_0,\, x_{n+1}) = \sum_{x_i \,\varepsilon\, s\,;\, x_j \,\varepsilon\, s'} c(x_i,\, x_j) -$$

$$\sum_{x_j \,\varepsilon\, s' \cap U} d(x_j) + \sum_{x_i \,\varepsilon\, s \cap U'} d(x_i).$$

In addition,

$$\sum_{x_i \,\varepsilon\, (\overline{N} - x_{n+1})} \bar{c}(x_i,\, x_{n+1}) = \sum_{x_i \,\varepsilon\, U'} d(x_i) =$$

$$= \sum_{x_i \,\varepsilon\, s' \cap U'} d(x_i) + \sum_{x_i \,\varepsilon\, s \cap U'} d(x_i).$$

By subtracting the two equalities, term by term, we obtain

$$\sum_{x_i \,\varepsilon\, (\overline{N} - x_{n+1})} \bar{c}(x_i,\, x_{n+1}) - \sum_{x_i \,\varepsilon\, \overline{s}\,;\, x_j \,\varepsilon\, \overline{s}'} \bar{c}(x_i\, x_j) = \sum_{x_i \,\varepsilon\, s' \cap U'} d(x_i) +$$

$$\sum_{x_i \,\varepsilon\, s' \cap M} d(x_j) - \sum_{x_i \,\varepsilon\, s\,;\, x_j \,\varepsilon\, s'} c(x_i\, x_j) = \sum_{x_i \,\varepsilon\, s'} d(x_i) - \sum_{x_i \,\varepsilon\, s\,;\, x_j \,\varepsilon\, s'} c(x_i\, x_j) \le 0.$$

Thus it has been verified that if (10) is valid, the cut $(\overline{N} - x_{n+1},\, x_{n+1})$ has a minimum capacity.

According to the theorem of Ford and Fulkerson, we have a flow φ, defined for $\overline{N}$, where

$$\sum_{x_i \,\varepsilon\, (\overline{N} - x_{n+1})} \varphi^*(x_i,\, x_{n+1}) =$$

$$= \sum_{x_i \,\varepsilon\, (\overline{N} - x_{n+1})} \bar{c}(x_i,\, x_{n+1}) = \sum_{x_i \,\varepsilon\, U'} d(x_i)$$

the asterisk indicating that the flow is a maximum.

According to the definition of flow, expression $\sum\limits_{x_{j}\epsilon \bar{N}} \varphi^{*}(x_i x_j)$ equals zero, hence if $x_i \epsilon U'$

$$\sum\limits_{x_j \epsilon \bar{N}} \varphi^{*}(x_i\, x_j) = \sum\limits_{x_j \epsilon N} \varphi^{*}(x_i\, x_j) + \varphi^{*}(x_i,\, x_{n+1}) =$$

$$= \sum\limits_{x_j \epsilon N} \varphi^{*}(x_i\, x_j) + d(x_i) = 0$$

that is,

$$\sum\limits_{x_j \epsilon N} \varphi^{*}(x_j\, x_i) = d(x_i).$$

If, instead, $x_i \epsilon U$ we have

$$0 = \sum\limits_{x_j \epsilon \bar{N}} \varphi^{*}(x_i\, x_j) =$$

$$= \sum\limits_{x_j \epsilon N} \varphi^{*}(x_j\, x_i) + \varphi^{*}(x_o\, x_i) \leq \sum\limits_{x_j \epsilon N} \varphi^{*}(x_j\, x_i) +$$

$$+ \bar{c}(_o\, x_i) = \sum\limits_{x_j \epsilon N} \varphi^{*})x_j\, x_i - d(x_i)$$

whence we obtain

$$\sum\limits_{x_j \epsilon N} \varphi^{*}(x_j\, x_i) \geq d(x_i)$$

In any case the flow $\varphi^{*}(x_i x_j)$ relative to the arcs of the graph G satisfies the condition (11); hence the theorem can be regarded as verified.

Section 8. Another Statement of the Gale Theorem

It is interesting to note that Gale found it possible to express the theorem in another form, namely:

The necessary and sufficient condition for the demand $d(x_i)$ to be achievable is that for each set Y of points belonging to U' there exists a flow φ such that

$$\sum_{x_i \, \varepsilon \, N} \varphi(x_i \, x_j) \geq d(x_j) \qquad \text{per } x_j \, \varepsilon \, U \qquad (13)$$

$$\sum_{x_i \, \varepsilon \, N} \sum_{x_j \, \varepsilon \, Y} \varphi(x_i \, x_j) \geq \sum_{x_i \, \varepsilon \, Y} d(x_j) \qquad (14)$$

Taking into account the definition of *demand*, the two foregoing conditions are obviously necessary. In order to ascertain whether they are also sufficient, it is enough to show that they imply the verification of condition (10) relative to the preceding expression.

Let us investigate a partition of the set N into two complementary sets (S,S′) and designate by X and X′ the two sub-sets of S and S′ respectively, consisting of points given by the inequality $d(x) \leqslant 0$; let us also designate by Y and Y′ the two sub-sets of S and S′ containing the positive demand points (it should be borne in mind that X and Y, X′ and Y′ complement each other with regard to S and S′).

According to conditions (13) and (14) we can write

$$\sum_{x_j \, \varepsilon \, X'} d(x_j) \leq \sum_{x_i \, \varepsilon \, N} \sum_{x_j \, \varepsilon \, X'} \varphi(x_i \, x_j) =$$

$$= \sum_{x_i \, \varepsilon \, X \cup Y} \sum_{x_j \, \varepsilon \, X'} \varphi(x_i \, x_j) + \sum_{x_i \, \varepsilon \, Y'} \sum_{x_j \, \varepsilon \, X'} \varphi(x_i \, x_j)$$

$$\sum_{x_j \, \varepsilon \, Y'} d(x_j) \leq \sum_{x_i \, \varepsilon \, N} \sum_{x_j \, \varepsilon \, Y'} \varphi(x_i \, x_j) =$$

$$= \sum_{x_i \, \varepsilon \, X \cup Y} \sum_{x_j \, \varepsilon \, Y'} \varphi(x_i \, x_j) + \sum_{x_i \, \varepsilon \, X'} \sum_{x_j \, \varepsilon \, Y'} \varphi(x_i \, x_j)$$

By summing the two inequalities term by term and keeping in mind that the sum of the last two addends equals zero, we obtain

$$\sum_{x_j \, \varepsilon \, X'} d(x_j) + \sum_{x_j \, \varepsilon \, Y'} d(x_j) = \sum_{x_i \, \varepsilon \, S'} d(x_i) \leq \sum_{x_i \, \varepsilon \, XUY} \sum_{x_j \, \varepsilon \, X'} \varphi(x_i \, x_j) +$$

$$+ \sum_{x_i \, \varepsilon \, XUY} \sum_{x_j \, \varepsilon \, Y'} \varphi(x_i \, x_j) = \sum_{x_i \, \varepsilon \, XUY} \sum_{x_j \, \varepsilon \, X'UY'} \varphi(x_i \, x_j) =$$

$$= \sum_{x_i \, \varepsilon \, S} \sum_{x_j \, \varepsilon \, S'} \varphi(x_i \, x_j) \leq \sum_{x_i \, \varepsilon \, S} \sum_{x_j \, \varepsilon \, S'} c(x_i \, x_j)$$

that is,

$$\sum_{x_i \, \varepsilon \, S'} d(x_i) \leq \sum_{x_i \, \varepsilon \, S} \sum_{x_j \, \varepsilon \, S'} c(x_i \, x_j)$$

which is condition (10).

Section 9. Definition of Potential in Transport Networks

We consider a connected graph G and introduce the following definitions:

1. A function $\pi(u)$ defined for all of the arcs of the graph is a difference of potential, if for all the cycles which can be considered in the graph, the sum of the values for π taken with their proper sign or the inverse one, (depending on whether the corresponding arc runs in its proper sense or in the opposite one), equals zero.

2. Let $p(x)$ be a function of the points of the graph connected with function π by the relationship

$$\pi(x_i x_j) = p(x_i) - p(x_j).$$

This is, by definition, a *potential function* of the graph.

(It is easy to derive the potential function from the function "difference of potential". In fact, by attributing to an arbitrary point x_0 the value $p(x_0)=0$, we can determine the values for $p(x)$ relative to adjacent points because we know the values for $\pi(x_0x_j)$; from each of these points we proceed in a similar fashion until all the points of the graph are covered. The condition which has to be satisfied by the difference of potential ensures that the procedure leads to a single value of $p(x)$ for each point.)

3. We associate points x_i of graph G with positive or negative numbers $q(x_i)$ which we call *excesses*.   Each function $\varphi(u)$ of arcs u is considered a flow consistent with the excesses if (a) its values are not negative and (b) if the sum of its values, relative to all of the arcs having a terminal at one point, taken with their proper sign or the opposite one depending on whether the corresponding arc is directed towards the point or originates from it, equals the excess relative to the point considered.

4. Finally, let each arc u be associated with a function $r(u_j)=r_j$ called *resistance* of the arc.

Section 10. The Dirichlet-Neumann Problem

Having set forth these preliminaries, we state the *Dirichlet problem*.

In a given graph determine the flow consistent with the assigned excesses, so that the function

$$\pi(u)=r(u) \ . \ \varphi(u)$$

be a difference of potential.

If we assume that the excesses are fixed only for certain points, while for the remaining points the potentials are fixed, we have a generalization of the problem stated above, known as the *Dirichlet-Neumann Problem*.

Let us now establish a condition ensuring the existence and uniqueness of the solution of the Dirichlet problem.

In the first place we note that the relationship

$$\pi(u) = r(u)\,\varphi(u)$$

can be written as a matrix by introducing the column vectors

$$\Pi = (\pi_1, \ \pi_2, \ \ldots \ , \ \pi_m);$$
$$\Phi = (\varphi_1, \varphi_2, \ \ldots \ , \ \varphi_m)$$

(we assume that there are m arcs in the graph) and the diagonal matrix

$$R = \| \ r_{ij} \ \|$$

where

$$r_{ij} = r_j \text{ if } i = j; \quad r_{ij} = 0 \text{ if } i \neq j$$
$$j = 1, 2, \ldots, m$$

We have

$$\Pi = R \cdot \Phi$$

and multiplying on the left by R^{-1}, the inverse matrix of R, we arrive at

$$\Phi = R^{-1} \cdot \Pi. \tag{15}$$

On the other hand, if S is the incidence matrix relative to the graph considered, and if P and Q are column vectors having as components respectively $p_i = p(x_i)$ that is, the values of the potential function, and $q_i = q(x_i)$, that is, the excess, then the conditions of the Dirichelet problem enable us to write

$$\Pi = S' \cdot P$$
$$Q = S \cdot \Phi \tag{16}$$

where S' is the transpose of S'. It is perhaps convenient to observe that in S' the rows consist of only two elements different from zero. These serve to indicate that the arc u_j originates in the point which labels the column concerning the element $+1$ and terminates in that which distinguishes the element -1.) Therefore the first relation in (16) is equivalent to definition 2 above, whereas the second assures the compatibility of the flow with the excess.

Using the first equation of (16) and relation (15) we can write

$$\Phi = R^{-1} \cdot S \cdot P. \tag{17}$$

Let us now remark that in general the system

$$Q = S \cdot \Phi \tag{18}$$

does not determine the vector Φ uniquely, because the unknowns generally exceeds the number of epuations. The Dirichlet problem will be solved if among the infinitely many solutions of (18), there can be found that one which satisfies (17). Combining (17) and (18), we have

$$Q = S \cdot R^{-1} \cdot S \cdot P$$

which represents a linear non-homogenous system of n equations in n unknowns, and it is known that it admits one and only one solution only if

$$\text{Det}(S \cdot R^{-1} \cdot S) \neq 0.$$

CHAPTER IV

Economic Applications

Section 1. Introduction

The Ford and Fulkerson algorithm enables us to determine flows with maximum values relative to a given network. It is obvious that if the arcs are interpreted as communication routes, if capacity of arcs is regarded as the maximum amount of materials which can be transported in a time unit through an arc of the transport network, if, finally, the value $\varphi(u)$ of the flow is interpreted as the quantity of material actually shipped in a time unit in arc u, it appears that determining maximum flow of a network is equivalent to solving the problem relative to the best way of utilizing a communication network, quite apart from economic considerations (e.g., transfer of an army from one place to another in a given area).

Yet, in accordance with what has been explicitly stated at the beginning of this book, we are interested essentially in introducing conditions of economic character.

For this purpose we return to the problems outlined earlier:

Section 2. The Transport Problem According to Hitchcock

There are m ports of embarkation x_i and n ports of destination y_j; we know that in x_i there are originally a_i ships, that b_j ships have to be sent to port y_j, and that, in addition, the cost for each voyage from x_i to y_j amounts to d_{ij} lire; we have to determine the number φ_{ij} of ships to be sent from x_i to y_j in order that the overall transportation cost

$$\Pi = \sum_{i=1} \sum_{j=1} d_{ij} \varphi_{ij}$$

remain a minimum.

Consequently, we have to find the integer values of the variables φ_{ij} which reduce the function Π to a minimum, knowing that the variables are subject to the following conditions

$$\sum_{i=1}^{m} \varphi_{ij} = b_j \qquad\qquad j = 1, 2, \ldots, n$$

$$\sum_{j=1}^{n} \varphi_{ij} = a_i \qquad\qquad i = 1, 2, \ldots, m$$

$$\varphi_{ij} \geqslant o \qquad\qquad \text{for each } i \text{ and } j$$

where a_i and b_j are obviously integer positive numbers.

Section 3. The Transport Problem According to Orden

In m places $x_i (i = 1, 2, \ldots, m)$ there is a surplus in merchandise a_i for a given period of time, and in n other places $y_j (j = m + 1, \ldots, m + n)$ there is a demand for b_j units of the same merchandise during the same period of time; c_{hk} is the capacity, relative to the above time interval, of the communication route which connects the two places (hence h and k may assume any whole value from one to $m + n$); moreover, d_{hk} is the cost of transporting a merchandise unit from one place to the other. We want to determine the quantity φ_{ij} which has to be transported in order that the transportation costs

$$\Pi = \sum_h \sum_k d_{hk} \varphi_{hh}$$

be a minimum, knowing that total surplus equals total demand, that is:

$$\sum_{i=1}^m a_i = \sum_{j=m+1}^{m+n} b_j = h$$

The problem consists in determining the values for φ_{hk} which reduce Π to a minimum and satisfy the relationships

$$0 \leq \varphi_{hk} \leq c_{hk}$$
$$\sum_{j=m+n}^{m+n} \varphi_{ij} = a_i$$
$$\sum_{i=1}^m \varphi_{ij} = b_j.$$

Section 4. Optimal Personnel Assignment

If x_i are the workers each of whom has to be assigned to one of y_j machines (hence $i, j = 1, 2 \ldots, n$), d_{ij} is the output of a worker x_i assigned to the machine y_j. Optimal assignment corresponds to that arrangement which maximizes the total (overall) output.

If

$$\varphi_{ij} = 1 \quad \text{when } x_i \text{ is assigned to } y_j$$
$$\varphi_{ij} = 0 \quad \text{in the other cases}$$

we have to maximize

$$\sum_{i=1}^{n}\sum_{j=1}^{n}d_{ij}\varphi_{ij}$$

knowing that

$$\sum_{i=1}^{n}\varphi_{ji} = 1;$$
$$\sum_{j=1}^{n}\varphi_{ij} = 1.$$

Section 5. The Warehouse Problem (Cahn) [1]

A given warehouse has a stock of certain merchandise. Let us consider its volume in a determined sequence of time intervals during which the volume of stock can change owing to purchases and sales. Knowing the sale and purchase price and the storage cost, and setting the condition that at the end of the period of time under consideration the stock be restored to its initial value, we want to know the volume of purchases and sales resulting in maximum profit.

Let p_i, q_i and r_i be, respectively, the unit price of sale, purchase and storage at time i. Let A and C be, respectively, the initial stock and the warehouse capacity (hence A $\leqslant$ C); and let

---

[1] A. S. Cahn, The Warehouse Problem, abstract, *Bulletin of the Am. Mathem. Soc.* Vol. 54, 1948, see also Berge .

a_i the quantity sold;

β_i the quantity purchased;

γ_i the residual stock after a sale;

δ_i the resulting stock after a purchase;

all with respect to time i.

We have to maximize the overall profit

$$G \equiv \sum_{i=1}^{n}(p_i a_i - q_i \beta_i - r_i \delta_i)$$

taking account of the conditions which restrict the variables, that is:

$$\begin{cases} A = a_1 + \gamma_1 \\ \delta_i = a_{i+1} + \gamma_{i+1} \\ \delta_i = \gamma_i + \beta_i \\ A = \gamma_n + \beta_n \\ \quad a_1 \geq 0 \\ \quad \beta_i \geq 0 \\ \quad \gamma_1 \geq 0 \\ 0 \leq \delta_1 \leq C \end{cases} \left. \begin{array}{l} \\ \\ \end{array} \right\} i = 1, \ldots . n - 1 \qquad (1)$$

Section 6. Standardization of Formulations

The problems investigated differ among each other in their mathematical formulation; yet it is possible, by means of a simple device, to reduce them to the following single formulation:

Maximize the function

$$L(\varphi) = \sum_{i=1}^{m}\sum_{j=1}^{n} d_{ij}\varphi_{ij}$$

knowing that

$$\begin{array}{l} \sum_{i=1}^{m} \varphi_{ij} = a_1 \\ \sum_{j=1}^{n} \varphi_{ij} = b_j \\ 0 \le \varphi_{ij} \le c_{ij} \end{array} \left. \begin{array}{l} \\ \\ \\ \end{array} \right\} \quad \begin{array}{l} i = 1, \ldots, m \\ \\ j = 2, \ldots, n \end{array} \qquad (2)$$

We first note that problems of minimum values can be formally reduced to problems of maximum values by taking

$$e_{ij} = h - d_{ij}$$

where $h \geqslant \{\max d_{ij}\}$
and where we assume $d_{ij} \geqslant 0$.

Then we consider the identity

$$\sum_{i=1}^{m} \sum_{i=1}^{n} e_{ij} \varphi_{ij} = h \quad \sum_{i=1}^{m} a_1 - \sum_{i=1}^{m} \sum_{j=1}^{n} d_{ij} \varphi_{ij}$$

and note that maximizing the first term is equivalent to minimizing

$$\sum_{i=1}^{m} \sum_{j=1}^{n} d_{ij} \varphi_{ij}.$$

At this point we can reformulate the foregoing problems in the following fashion, deriving the unique formulation mentioned above.

1. For Hitchcock's problem we substitute the constants d_{ij} for e_{ij} and assume $c_{ij} = \infty$;

2. For the Orden problem, it is enough to substitute e_{ij} for d_{ij} ;

3. For the personnel assignment problem, we bear in mind that

$$c_{ij} = \begin{cases} 1 \\ 0 \end{cases}$$

4. The warehouse problem requires some special considerations which it is expedient to postpone for the sake of clarity (see Section 8). Let us only note here that a_i, β_i, γ_i, δ_i can be assimilated to φ_{ij}, and that conditions (1) (excepting the second and the third) are equivalent to (2).

Section 7. Existence of a Solution

At this point we may wonder whether the problem is soluble. Let us therefore consider the following theorem:

The necessary and sufficient conditions for a solution of this problem require that a_i, b_j and c_{ij} be non-negative, satisfy the equality

$$\sum_{j=1}^{n} b_j = \sum_{i=1}^{m} a_i$$

and, moreover,

$$\sum_{i=1}^{m} \max \{ a_i , \sum_{j=J} c_{ij} \} \geq \sum_{j=J} b_j \qquad (3)$$

where the summations relative to j are referred to any of the sub-sets J of the set $\{1, 2, \ldots, n\}$.

The latter condition, less evident than the others, is derived from Gale's theorem. In order to realize this, one should examine the first considerations of the following Section and interpret b_j as demands.

Section 8. The Hungarian Algorithm

Let us now expound the so-called "Hungarian Algo-rithm"[1] availing ourselves essentially of the terminology proper to the theory of graphs.

Let us consider a transport network consisting of two sets of points $x_1, \ldots, x_m$ and $y_1 \ldots, y_n$, the initial point x_0 and the terminal point y_0.

The initial point is connected to each point x_i by means of arcs with a capacity c_{0i}; each x_i is connected to each y_j by means of arcs with a capacity c_{ij} and, finally, y_j is connected to the terminal point y_0 by means of arcs with a capacity c_{j0}.

Let us now consider a flow $\varphi(u)$, a function of the arc u, where the terminal arcs are saturated, that is,

$$
\begin{aligned}
\varphi(x_o x_i) \quad &= c_{oi} \\
\varphi(y_j x_o) \quad &= c_{jo} \\
0 \leq \varphi(x_i y_j) &\leqslant c_{ij}
\end{aligned}
$$

After fixing the constants d_{ij} we consider the function

$$
L(\varphi) = \sum_{i=1}^{m} \sum_{j=1}^{n} d_{ij} \varphi(x_i x_j)
$$

[1] See:

H. W. Kuhn, *The Hungarian Method for the Assignment Problem*, Naval Res. Quarterly, 2, 1955.

Ford-Fulkerson, *A Simple Algorithm for Finding Maximal Network Flows and an Application to the Hitchcock Problem*, Canadian J. of Math., 9, 1957.

Ford-Fulkerson, *Solving the Transportation Problem*, Man. Science, 3, 1956.

We want to determine φ in such a way that $L(\varphi)$ becomes maximized.

It is worth noting that according to these hypotheses the above problem coincides with the preceding one; in fact, we know that by the conservation property of flows we must have

$$\sum_{j=1}^{n} \varphi(x_i y_j) = \varphi(x_o x_i)$$
$$\sum_{i=1}^{m} \varphi(x_i y_j) = \varphi(y_j y_o)$$

hence if

$$\varphi(x_i y_j) = \varphi_{ij}$$
$$c_{oi} = a_i$$
$$c_{jo} = b_j$$

we find that the above formulation conforms with that of Section 6.

For the particular case of the warehouse problem we have to plot a graph considering as many points x_i as there are instances of sales or purchases. Then we add a point z representing the market and we introduce the initial and terminal points y_o and y_1.

The points x_i are connected with z by means of arcs $x_i \rightarrow z$ (for sales) or $z \rightarrow x_i$ (for purchases); if x_i and x_{i+1} represent sales and purchases at a given instant, they must be connected by means of arc $x_i \rightarrow x_{i+1}$; finally, each purchase point has to be connected by means of an arc to the sales point of the following successive time interval.

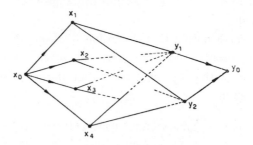

Fig. 16

Thus, $\alpha_i, \beta_i, \gamma_i, \delta_i$ can be regarded as values of $\varphi(u)$ because they satisfy the conditions which define the flow (in particular, the conservation property);

Figure 16 shows the graph which characterizes the first three problems, while Fig. 17 shows the graph relative to the warehouse problem.

Let us return to our previous considerations.

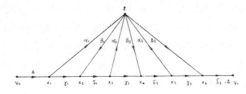

Fig. 17

In addition to the main problem (maximize $L(\varphi)$) we investigate the following problem:

Given a function $\gamma(u) \geqslant 0$, which satisfies the condition

$$\gamma(x_o x_i) + \gamma(x_i y_j) + \gamma(y_j y_o) \geqslant d_{ij} \tag{4}$$

we take into consideration the function

$$c(\gamma) = \sum_{i=1}^{m} c_{oi}\ \gamma(x_o x_i) + \sum_{i=1}^{m} \sum_{j=1}^{n} c_{ij}\ \gamma(x_i y_j) +$$
$$+ \sum_{j=1}^{n} c_{jo}\ \gamma\ (y_j y_o).$$

We want to determine γ in order to minimize $c(\gamma)$.

Under this assumption, the problem of determining maximum flow (that is, the flow which maximizes $L(\varphi)$) is based on the following theorems:

THEOREM I: If φ and γ are so chosen that

$$L(\varphi) = c(\gamma)$$

then φ is the maximum flow and γ reduces $c(\gamma)$ to a minimum.

To prove this let us show that for each selection of φ and γ we have

$$L(\varphi) \leqslant c(\gamma)$$

Let us note that from (4) we obtain immediately

$$d_{ij}\varphi(x_i y_j) \leqslant \gamma(y_i y_o)\varphi(x_i y_i) +$$
$$+ \gamma(x_i y_j)\varphi(x_i y_j) + \gamma(x_o x_i)\varphi(x_i y_j).$$

By summing these relationships, term by term, for each i and j we have

$$L(\varphi) = \sum_i \sum_j d_{ij}\varphi(x_i y_j) \leq \sum_i \gamma(y_j y_o)\sum_i \varphi(x_i y_i) +$$
$$+ \sum_i \sum_j \gamma(x_i y_j) + \sum_i \gamma(x_o x_i)\sum_j \varphi(x_i y_i);$$

on the other hand, taking account of the conservation property of the flow, we have

$$\sum_i \varphi(x_i y_j) = \varphi(y_j y_o) \qquad \text{and} \qquad \sum_j \varphi(x_i y_j) = \varphi(x_o x_i)$$

and hence we can write

$$L(\varphi) \leq \sum_j \gamma(y_j y_o) \varphi(y_j y_o) + \sum_i \sum_j \gamma(x_i y_j) \varphi(x_i y_j) +$$
$$+ \sum_i \gamma(x_o x_i) \varphi(x_o x_i) \leqslant c(\gamma).$$

This relationship permits us to affirm that each $L(\varphi)$ will not exceed the minimum value of $c(\gamma)$ and, conversely, $c(\gamma)$ cannot be less than the maximum value for $L(\varphi)$. Thus, if there is an equality for a specific pair of γ and φ, it will correspond to the above maximum and minimum conditions, respectively.

Let us first consider the function γ which is defined as follows

$$\gamma(x_o x_i) = \max d_{ij}$$
$$\gamma(y_j y_o) = \max [0; d_{ij} - \gamma(x_o x_i)] \qquad (5)$$
$$\gamma(x_i y_j) = \max [0; d_{ij} - \gamma(x_o x_i) - \gamma(y_j y_o)]$$

thus, condition (4)'is certainly satisfied. Let us now group the arcs $(x_i y_j)$ into the following three sets:

I_1 contains the arcs where

$$\gamma(x_o x_i) + \gamma(y_j y_o) = d_{ij}$$
$$\text{and hence } \gamma(x_i y_j) = 0$$

I_2 contains the arcs where

$$\gamma(x_o x_i) + \gamma(y_j y_o) > d_{ij}$$
$$\text{and hence } \gamma(x_i y_j) = 0$$

I_3 contains the arcs where

$$\gamma(x_o x_i) + \gamma(y_j y_o) + \gamma(x_i y_j) = d_{ii}$$
$$\text{and hence } \gamma(x_i y_j) > 0.$$

We now consider a new graph $\bar{G}$ derived from G by replacing the original capacity with the following[1]

$$\left.\begin{array}{l} \bar{c}_{oi} = c_{oi} - \sum_j c_{ij} \\ \bar{c}_{jo} = c_{jo} - \sum_j c_{ij} \end{array}\right\} \quad \begin{array}{l} \text{Where the summations pertain to} \\ \text{arcs belonging to the set } I_3 \text{ defined} \\ \text{above} \end{array} \qquad (6)$$

$$\bar{c}_{ij} = \left\{ \begin{array}{l} c_{ij} \text{ for arcs belonging to } I_1 \\ 0 \text{ for arcs belonging to } I_2 \text{ or } I_3. \end{array} \right.$$

This is equivalent to eliminating the arcs of G belonging to sets I_2 and I_3, to leaving unchanged the capacities of arcs $(x_i y_j)$ belonging to I_1 and varying the capacities of the terminal arcs by reducing them by the capacities of the adjacent arcs belonging to I_3.

It may occur that, in accordance with γ considered above, graph G produces a flow φ capable of saturating all the terminal arcs; in this case we can show that γ renders $c(\gamma)$ a minimum and the function

$$\varphi = \left\{ \begin{array}{l} \bar{\varphi}(x_i y_j) \text{ for arcs belonging to } I_1 \text{ and} \\ c_{ij} \quad \text{ for arcs belonging to } I_3. \end{array} \right.$$

increases $L(\varphi)$ to a maximum; hence the problem can be regarded as solved with respect to graph G.

On the other hand, if in accordance with an assigned γ there is no flow $\bar{\varphi}$ capable of saturating the terminal arcs we prove that it is possible to determine a function γ' where

$$c(\gamma') \leqslant c(\gamma).$$

---

[1]We shall afterwards justify the introduction of graph G and the special way of defining it.

With this function we repeat the search for a flow capable of saturating the terminal arcs. We are, therefere, bound to arrive at one of the two cases mentioned above. In each of them we have to proceed as stated previously.

Let us now justify the particular definition of graph $\bar{G}$

After selecting function γ of the type defined in (5), subtract from and add to $c(\gamma)$ the quantity

$$\sum_{i,j\,\varepsilon\,I_3} [\gamma(x_0\,x_i) + \gamma(y_j\,y_0) + \gamma(x_i\,y_j)]\, c_{ij}$$

Taking account of the definition of I_3, we can write

$$c(\gamma) - \sum_{i,j\,\varepsilon\,I_3} [\gamma(x_0\,x_i) + \gamma(y_j\,y_0) + \gamma(x_i\,y_j)]\, c_{ij} + \sum_{i,j\,\varepsilon\,I_3} d_{ij}\,c_{ij}$$

or, by expanding $c(\gamma)$,

$$\sum_{i=1}^{m} \gamma(x_0\,x_i)\,c_{oi} + \sum_{i=1}^{m}\sum_{j=1}^{n} \gamma(x_i\,y_j)\,c_{ij} + \sum_{j=1}^{n} \gamma(y_j\,y_0)\,c_{jo} -$$

$$- \sum_{i,j\,\varepsilon\,I_3} [\gamma(x_0\,x_i) + \gamma(y_j\,y_0) + \gamma(x_i\,y_j)]\, c_{ij} + \sum_{i,j\,\varepsilon\,I_3} d_{ij}\,c_{ij}$$

By placing $\gamma(x_0 x_i)$, $\gamma(y_j y_0)$ outside the bracket and bearing in mind that

$$\sum_{i=1}^{m}\sum_{j=1}^{n} \gamma(x_i\,y_j)\,c_{ij} = \sum_{i,j\,\varepsilon\,I_3} \gamma(x_i\,y_j)\,c_{ij}$$

since

$$\gamma(x_i\,y_j) = 0 \qquad\qquad i, j\,\varepsilon\,I_1 \cup I_2\,,$$

we have

$$\sum_{i=1}^{m} [c_{oi} - \sum_{j/(i,j)\varepsilon I_3} c_{ij}]\,\gamma(x_0\,x_i) +$$

$$\sum_{j=1}^{n} [c_{jo} - \sum_{i/(i,j)\varepsilon I_3} c_{ij}]\,\gamma(y_j\,y_0) + \sum_{i,j\,\varepsilon\,I_3} d_{ij}\,c_{ij}$$

The expressions in square brackets are $\bar{c}_{oi}$ and $\bar{c}_{jo}$ defined, in (6); hence we can write

$$\sum_{i=1}^{m} \bar{c}_{oi} \gamma(x_o x_i) + \sum_{j=1}^{n} \bar{c}_{jo} \gamma(y_j y_o) + \sum_{i,j \, \varepsilon \, I_3} c_{ij} d_{ij}$$

$\bar{c}_{oi}$ and $\bar{c}_{jo}$ are interpreted as flow values; for the conservation property we can write

$$\sum_{i=1}^{m} (\sum_{j=1}^{n} \bar{c}_{ij}) \gamma(x_o x_i) + \sum_{j=1}^{n} (\sum_{i=1}^{m} \bar{c}_{ij}) \gamma(y_j y_o) + \sum_{i,j \, \varepsilon \, I_3} c_{ij} d_{ij} =$$

$$= \sum_{i=1}^{m} \sum_{j=1}^{n} \bar{c}_{ij} [\gamma(x_o x_i + \gamma(y_j y_o)] + \sum_{i,j \, \varepsilon, I_3} c_{ij} d_{ij}$$

Keeping in mind the last part of (6) as well as the fact that in I_1 we have

$$\gamma(x_o x_i) + \gamma(y_j y_o) = d_{ij}$$

we finally obtain (it should be noted that the second addend equals zero because in I_2, $\bar{c}_{ij} = 0$):

$$\sum_{i,j \, \varepsilon \, I_1} \bar{c}_{ij} d_{ij} + \sum_{i,j \, \varepsilon \, I_2} \bar{c}_{ij} d_{ij} +$$

$$\sum_{i,j \, \varepsilon \, I_3} c_{ij} d_{ij} = \sum_{i=1}^{m} \sum_{j=1}^{n} c_{ij} d_{ij} = L[\varphi] \quad (7)$$

It appears in conclusion that a graph $\bar{G}$ constructed on the basis of (6) ensures maximum flow $\bar{\varphi}$ which saturates the terminal arcs and makes it possible to define a quantity $L(\varphi)$, equalling $c(\gamma)$ together with the values of c_{ij} for $(i,j) \epsilon I_3$; thus, by theorem I is we are sure that $L(\varphi)$ is a maximum.

Following is the demonstration of the two statements on pages 88 and 89.

THEOREM II:

If for a certain function γ, graph $\overline{G}$ yields a flow φ which saturates the terminal arcs, γ renders $c(\gamma)$ a minimum and for the original graph G the flow reducing $L(\varphi)$ to a maximum is given by

$$\varphi = \begin{cases} \varphi(x_i y_j) & \text{if } (x_i y_j) \text{ belongs to } I_1 \text{ or } I_2 \\ c_{ij} & \text{if } (x_i y_j) \text{ belongs to } I_3 \end{cases}$$

To prove this it is sufficient to compute the function $L(\varphi)$ for the values of φ defined above and show that it equals $c(\gamma)$.

We have

$$L(\varphi) = \sum_{I_1 \cup I_2} d_{ij} \overline{\varphi} \ (x_i \, y_j) + \sum_{I_3} d_{ij} c_{ij}$$

and proceeding from (7) we derive

$$L(\varphi) = c(\gamma).$$

THEOREM III:

If for a given function γ, graph $\overline{G}$ does not yield a maximum flow $\overline{\varphi}$ which saturates the terminal arcs, it is always possible to find a new function γ' according to which the inequality $c(\gamma') < c(\gamma)$ is verified.

Let us assume that φ does not saturate the terminal arcs and that it is a maximum for graph $\overline{G}$; thus we can determine a cut $[Y, C(Y)]$ where, for example,

$$Y = \{x_1, x_2, \ldots, x_r, y_1, y_2, \ldots, y_s, y_0\}$$

for which the relationship

$$\Gamma[Y, C(Y)] = \varphi < \sum_{i=1}^{m} \bar{c}_{0i}$$

is true. (The equality is derived from the Ford and Fulkerson theorem, while the inequality follows from the hypothesis that the terminal arcs are not saturated.)

Let us now set

$$\gamma'(x_o x_i) = \begin{cases} \gamma(x_o x_i) & \text{for } i = 1, 2, \ldots, r \\ \gamma(x_o x_i) - 1 & \text{for } i = r + 1, \ldots, m \end{cases}$$

$$\gamma'(y_j y_o) = \begin{cases} \gamma(y_j y_o) & \text{for } j = 1, 2 \ldots, s \\ \gamma(y_j y_o) + 1 & \text{for } j = s + 1, \ldots, n \end{cases}$$

$$\gamma'(x_i y_j) = \begin{cases} \gamma(x_i y_j) - 1 \text{ for arcs belonging to } I_3 \text{ which connect points } x_i \text{ of } Y \text{ to points } y_j \text{ not belonging to } Y; \\ \gamma(x_i y_j) + 1 \text{ for arcs belonging to } I_1 \text{ or } I_3 \text{ connecting points } x_i \text{ not contained in } Y \text{ to points } y_j \text{ of } Y; \\ \gamma(x_i y_j) \quad \text{in all the other cases.} \end{cases}$$

Thus we obtain a new function γ' with non-negative terms (in fact, in those cases where we subtract 1, the values of γ are certainly positive) and still satisfying the basic condition (4), which we deduce by analyzing, in the various possible cases, the total variations undergone by the first term of (4).

		$\Delta \gamma \, (x_o \, x_i)$	$\Delta \gamma \, (x_i \, y_j)$	$\Delta \gamma \, (y_j \, y_o)$	Δ total
I_1	$(x_i \, y_j) \, \varepsilon \, Y$	0	0	0	0
	$\begin{cases} x_i \, \varepsilon \, Y \\ y_j \, \varepsilon \, C(Y) \end{cases}$	0	$+1$	0	$+1$
	$\begin{cases} x_i \, \varepsilon \, C(Y) \\ y_j \, \varepsilon \, Y \end{cases}$	-1	0	$+1$	0
	$(x_i \, y_j) \, \varepsilon \, C(Y)$	-1	$+1$	0	0
I_2	$(x_i \, y_j) \, \varepsilon \, Y$	0	0	0	0
	$\begin{cases} x_i \, \varepsilon \, Y \\ y_j \, \varepsilon \, C(Y) \end{cases}$	0	0	$+1$	$+1$
	$\begin{cases} x_i \, \varepsilon \, C(Y) \\ y_j \, \varepsilon \, Y \end{cases}$	-1	0	0	-1
	$(x_i \, y_j) \, \varepsilon \, C(Y)$	-1	0	$+1$	0
I_3	$(x_i \, y_j) \, \varepsilon \, Y$	0	0	0	0
	$\begin{cases} x_i \, \varepsilon \, Y \\ y_j \, \varepsilon \, C(Y) \end{cases}$	0	-1	$+1$	0
	$\begin{cases} x_i \, \varepsilon \, C(Y) \\ y_j \, \varepsilon \, Y \end{cases}$	-1	$+1$	0	0
	$(x_i \, y_j) \, \varepsilon \, C(Y)$	-1	0	$+1$	0

We see from this table that, excepting one case, the total of Δ is non-negative; on the other hand, in I_2 we are certain on the basis of our hypotheses that

$$\gamma (x_o x_i) + \gamma (x_i y_j) + \gamma (y_j y_o) > d_{ij}$$

and hence a variation by -1 does not contradict (4). In conclusion, γ' still satisfies the conditions placed upon γ in the dual problem; hence it is necessary only to verify the relationship $c(\gamma') < c(\gamma)$. For this purpose let us expand the expression for $c(\gamma')$ in the following way:

$$c(\gamma') = \sum_i c_{oi}\, \gamma'_{oi} + \sum_j c_{jo}\, \gamma'_{jo} + \sum_i \sum_j c_{ij}\, \gamma'_{ij} =$$

$$= \sum_{i \leq r} c_{oi}\, \gamma_{oi} + \sum_{i > r} c_{oi}(\gamma_{oi} - 1) +$$

$$\sum_{j \leq s} c_{jo}\, \gamma_{jo} + \sum_{j > s} c_{jo}(\gamma_{jo} + 1) +$$

$$+ \sum_{\substack{I_3 \\ i \leq r;\, j > s}} c_{ij}(\gamma_{ij} - 1) + \sum_{\substack{I_1 \\ i > r;\, j \leq s}} c_{ij}(\gamma_{ij} + 1) +$$

$$\sum_{\substack{I_3 \\ i > r;\, j \leq s}} c_{ij}(\gamma_{ij} + 1) + \sum_{*} c_{ij}\, \gamma_{ij}$$

(where, for brevity, we have set $\gamma(x_i y_j) = \gamma_{ij}$, etc., and where the asterisk of the last summation refers to the arcs which were not included in the other summations). By expanding and summing up we obtain

$$c(\gamma') = c(\gamma) - \sum_{i > r} \bar{c}_{oi} + \sum_{j > s} \bar{c}_{jo} + \sum_{i > r;\, j \leq s} \bar{c}_{ij} = c(\gamma) - \sum_{i=1}^{m} \bar{c}_{oi} +$$

$$+ \sum_{i \leq r} \bar{c}_{oi} + \sum_{j > s} \bar{c}_{jo} + \sum_{i > r;\, j \leq s} \bar{c}_{ji}$$

But for the three last summations

$$\Gamma[Y, C(Y)] < \sum_{i=1}^{m} \bar{c}_{oi}$$

is valid, and hence follows

$$c(\gamma') - c(\gamma) < 0 \quad \text{c.v.d.}$$

Section 9. A Numerical Example

Let us examine the graph in Fig. 18a and assume that
the values for d_{ij} are as follows

$$
\begin{array}{c}
\quad\ \ j \\
i\ \
\begin{array}{|ccc|}
\hline
2 & 3 & 1 \\
4 & 2 & 3 \\
1 & 5 & 1 \\
3 & 1 & 2 \\
\hline
\end{array}
\end{array}
$$

It is easily deduced that the initial function has as values
(recalling (5)):

$$\gamma(x_o x_i) = 3, 4, 5, 3$$

$\gamma(y_j y_o)$ and $\gamma(x_i x_j)$ equalling zero.

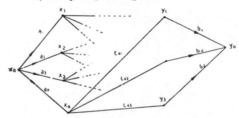

Fig. 18a

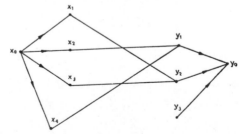

Fig. 18b

Let us now determine the sets I_1, I_2 and I_3. For the differences

$$D = d_{ij} - \gamma(x_o x_i) - \gamma(y_j y_o)$$

we have

	j		
	$D < 0$	$D = 0$	$D < 0$
i	$D = 0$	$D < 0$	$D < 0$
	$D < 0$	$D = 0$	$D < 0$
	$D = 0$	$D < 0$	$D < 0$

We conclude that

$$I_1 = \{(x_1 y_2); (x_2 y_1); (x_3 y_2); (x_4 y_1)\}$$
$$I_2 = \{\text{the remaining arcs}\}$$
$$I_3 = 0$$

hence

$$\begin{aligned}
\bar{c}_{oi} &= c_{oi} & i &= 1, 2, 3, 4 \\
\bar{c}_{jo} &= \bar{c}_{jo} & j &= 1, 2, 3 \\
\bar{c}_{12} &= c_{12} \\
\bar{c}_{21} &= c_{21} \\
\bar{c}_{32} &= c_{32} \\
\bar{c}_{41} &= c_{41}
\end{aligned}$$

Finally, $\bar{c}_{11}$, $\bar{c}_{13}$, $\bar{c}_{22}$, $\bar{c}_{23}$, $\bar{c}_{31}$, $\bar{c}_{33}$, $\bar{c}_{42}$, $\bar{c}_{43}$ equal zero.

Thus we obtain graph $\overline{G}$ of Fig. 18b in which one may proceed to look for the maximum flow with the aid of the Ford and Fulkerson algorithm. If this flow saturates the terminal arcs, the problem is solved; otherwise, in accordance with the above rules, a new function is found and the procedure is started anew.

Section 10. The Model of Industrial Interdependence

We comment briefly on a model developed by N. Leontief. This model is derived with the aid of appropriate assumptions regarding the rate of production for the industries of a given economic system for the purpose of obtaining preestablished quantities of goods for the final economic sectors.

The model is well known and its brief description in this book is justified because of the opportunity it affords us to apply the theory of graphs.

This model is based on the following hypotheses:

1.   The total net production of each industry equals the total amount of its products consumed by other industries, increased by the quantity appointed for the final sectors.

2.   Under static equilibrium conditions, the value of the products of each industry must equal the sum of the values of products and services absorbed.

3.   The quantities of production factors are directly proportional to the quantities produced.

Let us assume that the foregoing hypotheses are acceptable and let us designate by X_i the net production of the i-th industry, by x_{ik} the production of the i-th industry absorbed by the k-th industry, by Y_i that part of the production of the i-th industry designed for the final sectors, by p_i, p_{ik} and q_i the prices of X_i, x_{ik} and Y_i, respectively, and finally by q_{ik} the proportionality coefficients assumed by the third hypothesis.

Then we can write

$$\left.\begin{array}{l} X_1 = x_{12} + x_{13} + \ldots + x_{14} + Y_1 \\ \cdots \cdots \cdots \cdots \cdots \cdots \cdots \cdots \cdots \\ X_i = x_{i1} + x_{i2} + \ldots + x_{i,i1} + x_{i,in} + \ldots + Y_i \\ X_n = x_{n1} + \ldots + x_{n,n-1} + Y_n \end{array}\right\} \quad (8)$$

$$\left.\begin{array}{l} p_1\, X_1 = x_{12}\, p_{12} + \ldots + Y_1\, q_1 \\ \cdots \cdots \cdots \cdots \cdots \cdots \cdots \\ p_n\, X_n = x_{n1}\, p_{n1} + \ldots + Y_n\, q_n \end{array}\right\} \quad \begin{array}{r}(9) \\ \\ (10)\end{array}$$

$$x_{ik} = q_{ik}\, X_k$$

Equations (8), (9) and (10) are the mathematical formulation of the first, second and third hypotheses, respectively.

Substituting expressions (10) into (8), we obtain

$$\left\{\begin{array}{l} X_1 = q_{11}\, X_1 + q_{12}\, X_2 + q_{13}\, X_3 + \ldots Y_1 \\ \cdots \cdots \cdots \cdots \cdots \cdots \cdots \cdots \cdots \\ X_i = q_{i1}\, X_1 + \ldots + Y_i \\ \cdots \cdots \cdots \cdots \cdots \cdots \cdots \cdots \cdots \\ X_n = q_{n1}\, X_1 \ldots + q_{n,n-1}\, X_{n-1} + q_{nn}\, X_n + Y_n \end{array}\right.$$

that is,

$$\left.\begin{array}{l} (1 - q_n)\, X_1 - q_{12}\, X_2 - \ldots - q_{1n}\, X_n = Y_1 \\ \cdots \cdots \cdots \cdots \cdots \cdots \cdots \cdots \cdots \\ - q_{n1}\, X_1 - q_{n2}\, X_2 - \ldots + (1 - q_{n4})\, X_n = Y_n \end{array}\right\} \quad (11)$$

By resolving according to Cramer's rule we obtain

$$
\left\{
\begin{array}{l}
X_1 = A_{11}\,Y_1 + A_{21}\,Y_2 + A_{31}\,Y_3 + \ldots A_{n1}\,Y_n \\
\cdot\ \cdot\ \cdot\ \cdot\ \cdot\ \cdot\ \cdot\ \cdot\ \cdot\ \cdot\ \cdot\ \cdot\ \cdot\ \cdot\ \cdot\ \cdot \\
X_i = A_{1i}\,Y_1 + A_{2i}\,Y_2 + \ldots + A_{ni}\,Y_n \\
X_n = A_{1n}\,Y_1 + \ldots + A_{nn}\,Y_n
\end{array}
\right. \tag{12}
$$

where A_{jk} is a typical element of the inverse matrix A^{-1} of the matrix of coefficients of the system (11).

It can be seen that we have thus solved the problem of determining the net total produce of various industries, the demand of the final economic sectors being known.

The system of equations (9) which has not been utilized in the computation introduces the required relationships between prices and produced and consumed quantities, under the assumption that the economic system is in static equilibrium.

Before changing to another subject, we deem it useful to make some remarks about the solvability of system(11) and the characteristics of its solution (12).

It should be borne in mind that, in practice, the number of unknowns and equations of system(11) is so high that direct verifications and controls are nearly impossible; this fact emphasizes the importance of the following considerations which offer simple criteria for deciding whether system (11) can be solved at all and whether a solution would be positive.

It is known that if we assume that all the Y_i do not equal zero and that matrix A of the coefficients is not singular, system **(11)** has one, and only one, solution. Now, it can be shown[1] that the last condition $(A \neq) \, 0$ is certainly true if

$$\sum_{i=1}^{n} q_{ij} < 1 \text{ for each } j$$

Once this has been established, we note that solution (12) is significant economically only if the X_i are positive. In this connection it has been shown[2] that if the economic system under consideration is "connected", that is, if there exists no partial group of industries independent of the remaining part of the system, the values obtained by means of (12) are positive. We can express this fact mathematically by saying that matrix A must be irreducible[3] and non-singular.

We are not going to prove the above statements; instead, we prefer to dwell upon the exposition of the following interesting application of the theory of graphs to Leontief's matrix analysis.

We consider a graph where the points represent individual industries, while the final economic sectors are represented by a single point (the consumer). We connect these points by means of arcs whose direction determines the flow of money between the two extreme points.

---

[1] M. A. Woodbury, *Properties of Leontief-type input-output matrices*, in "Economic Activity Analysis", J. Wiley, N. Y. page 343.

[2] M. A. Woodbury, op. cit. page 349.

[3] It should be borne in mind that a matrix is said to be "irreducible" if it is impossible to write it as $\left\| \begin{array}{cc} B & C \\ O & D \end{array} \right\|$ by applying the same substitution to the lines and columns. B and D are square matrices and O is a zero-matrix.

Thus, the arcs with a terminal at the point corresponding to consumption, are all running from this point; instead, two industries are usually connected by two arcs which run in opposite directions.   This shows that each of these industries consumes a part of the production of the other (see Fig. 12, where x_1 is the point marking consumption, while x_2, x_3 and x_4 represent industries).

Thereupon we consider all the arborescences (or *directed trees*) having their roots in the consumption point and associate each of their arcs with the intensity of the money flow, taken as an absolute value, and derivable from the Leontief matrix; then we define the product of the flows relative to its arcs as *arborescence value* (one should bear in mind what was said in the Section "Trees and Tree Derivations.")

We know that the sum of the values of all of the arborescence mentioned above equals the determinant which can be associated with the Leontief matrix.   Because the value of each arborescence is positive, we can affirm that such a determinant is certainly greater than zero provided there exists at least one arborescence.

Moreover, it is possible to show[1] that if there exists an arborescence derivable from the graph corresponding to N industries, there also exist arborescences relative to a partial group of industries derivable from the given one; this means that all of the principal minors of the Leontief matrix are positive if the determinant derived from the matrix itself is positive.

---

[1] T. M. Whitin, *An Economic Application of "Matrices and Trees"*, in "Economic Activity Analysis", 1954, J. Wiley.

Thus we have established the necessary and sufficient condition given by Georgescu-Roegen for the existence of static equilibrium, which can be worded as follows:

"The necessary and sufficient conditions in order that the solution of the Leontief linear system correspond to a situation of static equilibrium consist in that the determinant associated with the matrix of coefficients as well as all of the principal minors derivable from it exceed zero"[1].

The impossibility of plotting the arborescence mentioned above is evidence of the presence of particular structures in the economic system; for example, such an impossibility takes place when the economy under investigation is "closed" as a whole or in part, that is, when all of the industries, or parts thereof, constitute a completely self-sufficient group which does not participate in exchanges with the consumption sector (see, for example, Fig. 19, where x_1 is the consumption sector).

The Georgescu-Roegen condition can be interpreted from an economic point of view; in fact, the condition according to which all of the principal minors must exceed zero is equivalent to saying that the industry groups corresponding to each minor must be capable of producing more than their requirements. If, for example, a princi-

[1] See:

D. Hawkins and H. A. Simon, Note: *Some Conditions of Macroeconomic Stability*, Econometrica, 1949, page 245.

Georgescu-Roegen, *Leontief's System in the Light of Recent Results*, Review of Economics and Statistics, 1950. In this article the condition is only outlined.

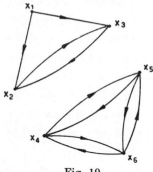

Fig. 19

pal minor containing the i-th and j-th industry is smaller than zero, this implies that the quantity of the i-th product required for producing a unit of the j-th product turns out to be smaller than that of the i-th one producible with the aid of a unit of the j-th good. Under such conditions the production of these two goods could not be carried on indefinitely.

Section 11. An Alternative of the Leontief Model

Problem 4 formulated in the beginning is very similar to that mentioned above. Let us show how it can be reduced to a classical problem related to electric circuits and how, with the aid of the theory of graphs, it is possible to find an efficient solution.

In the first place, let us state the mathematical formulation of problem 4).

Industries x_i and products y_j $(i = 1 \ldots, m; j = 1 \ldots, n)$ are represented by points in a graph. The points of products are connected with the points of industries so that the arc (x_iy_j) indicates that industry x_i produces merchandise y_j while arc (y_jx_i) shows that merchandise y_j is consumed by industry x_i. Then each arc is associated with conductance c_{ij} which represents the quantity of goods consumed or produced by an industry when operating at unit intensity. Conductances take the sign $+$ if they indicate production, and the sign $-$ where they indicate consumption.

We have

$$q(y_j) = a_j - \beta_j$$

where a_j and β_j indicate, respectively, the initial and final level of availability of y_j; we denote with $p(x_i)$ the intensity with which industry x_i must operate in order to obtain the availability variations sought and set $p(y_j) = 0$. If $\varphi(y_j, x_i)$ $\varphi(y_j, x_i)$ and $\varphi(x_i, y_j)$ denote, respectively, the quantities of merchandise y_j consumed and produced by industry x_i, we can write

$$\varphi(y_jx_i) = c_{ji}[p(y_j) - p(x_i)]$$
$$\varphi(x_iy_j) = c_{ij}[p(x_i) - p(y_j)].$$

All this amounts to determining the flow in a graph where the excesses for certain points and the potentials for certain others are known, that is, we are dealing with the Dirichlet-Neumann problem.

It should be noted that this problem has long ago been formulated and solved in electrical engineering for the study of electric circuits. We may therefore avail ourselves of the computation procedures devised by those who studied these problems; particularly interesting is the method proposed by Gabriel Kron for the analysis of stationary electric circuits, which uses certain topological properties of graphs.

We shall not describe the practical rules set forth by this method but refer the reader interested in further details to works on electrical engineering dealing with this subject. (It may be useful to examine the book *"Matrix Analysis of Electric Networks"* by P. Le Corbeiller, Harvard University Press, 1950, where the Kron method is expounded in an exhaustive fashion. The same work is also available in French, published by Dunod in Paris.)

Here, we shall merely mention that in order to simplify the solution of the system of linear equations derived from the problem, a square matrix called "transformation matrix" is set up with the aid of the cyclomatic properties of the image graph.

References

C. Berge, *Theorie des graphes et ses applications*, Dunod, Paris, 1958.

Bott and Mayberry, "Matrices and Trees", in *Economic Activity Analysis*, Oskar Morgenstern, ed., John Wiley & Sons, New York, 1954.

A. S. Cahn, "The Warehouse Problem," *Bulletin of the American Mathematical Society* **54** (1948).

R. Debry and S. Huyberechts, "Quelques aspects de la theorie des graphes," in *Cahiers du Centre d'Etudes de Recherche Operationnelle*, Bruxelles, 1959.

L. R. Ford and D. R. Fulkerson, "Maximal Flow through a Network," *Can. J. Math.* **8** (1956).

Ford-Fulkerson, "A Simple Algorithm for Finding Maximal Network Flows and an Application to the Hitchcock Problem," *Can. J. Math.* **9** (1957).

Ford-Fulkerson, "Solving the Transportation Problem," *Management Science* **3** (1956).

David Gale, "A Theorem on Flows in Networks," *Pacific J. Math.* **7** (1957).

Georgescu-Roegen, "Leontief's System in the Light of Recent Results," *Review of Economics and Statistics* (1950).

D. Hawkins and H. A. Simon, "Note: Some Conditions of Macroeconomic Stability," *Econometrica*, **245** (1949).

F. L. Hitchcocks, "The Distribution of a Product from Several Sources to Numerous Localities," *J. Math. Phys.* **20** (1941).

D. Konig, *Theorie der endlichen und unendlichen Graphen*, Chelsea Publishing Co., 1950.

H. W. Kuhn, "The Hungarian Method for the Assignment Problem," *Naval Res. Quarterly* **2** (1955).

P. Le Corbeiller, *Matrix Analysis of Electric Networks*, Harvard University Press, 1950.

Monge, "Deblai et Ramblai," *Memoires de l'Academic des Sciences*, 1781.

A. Orden, "The Transshipment Problem," *Management Science* **2** (1956).

H. M. Trent, "A Note on the Enumeration and Listing of All Possible Trees in a Connected Linear Graph," *Proc. Nat. Acad. Sci. U. S.* **40** (1959).

D. F. Votaw and A. Orden, "The Personnel Assignment Problem," *Scoop Symposium on Linear Inequalities and Programming*, Washington, 1952.

T. M. Whitin, "An Economic Application of 'Matrices and Trees'", in *Economic Activity Analysis*, Oskar Morgenstern, ed., John Wiley & Sons, New York, 1954.

M. A. Woodbury, "Properties of Leontief-type Input-Output Matrices," in *Economic Activity Analysis*, Oskar Morgenstern, ed., John Wiley & Sons, New York, 1954, p. 343.

Index of Definitions